Nurturing Wholeness with Primary Food for Balanced Living

Mr. Miller

Published by Leon M. Miller II, 2023.

While every precaution has been taken in the preparation of this book, the publisher assumes no responsibility for errors or omissions, or for damages resulting from the use of the information contained herein.

NURTURING WHOLENESS WITH PRIMARY FOOD FOR BALANCED LIVING

First edition. November 20, 2023.

Copyright © 2023 Mr. Miller.

ISBN: 979-8223971306

Written by Mr. Miller.

Table of Contents

To my father **Leon M. Miller** [*aka Jack Frost 01/11/1965 - 08/28/2012*] the one who was a father & brother to many. The Patriarch. The Golden Heart. The Great Hugger. His journey of dealing with his health is what led me to go further into not only helping my family & I, but also as many people that this ripple effect I'm making will reach. I love you Dad!

Nurturing Wholeness with Primary Food for Balanced Living

Introduction

1.1 Understanding the Whole Self

In order to cultivate vibrant lives, it is essential to understand the concept of the whole self. The whole self refers to the interconnectedness of various aspects of our lives, including relationships, careers, fitness, and spirituality. These four dimensions are not separate entities but rather intertwined elements that contribute to our overall well-being.

The Interconnectedness of Relationships, Careers, Fitness, and Spiri- tuality

OUR RELATIONSHIPS, careers, fitness, and spirituality are all interconnected and have a profound impact on each other. When one aspect of our lives is out of balance, it can affect other areas as well. For example, if we are experiencing difficulties in our relationships, it can lead to stress and emotional turmoil, which can then impact our performance in our careers and our overall physical and mental well-being.

On the other hand, when we nurture and cultivate healthy relationships, it can have a positive ripple effect on other areas of our lives. Strong and supportive relationships provide a sense of belonging, love, and emotional support, which can enhance our overall happiness and well-being. This, in turn, can positively influence our careers, as we feel more motivated, confident, and supported in pursuing our professional goals.

Similarly, engaging in regular exercise and maintaining physical fitness can have a profound impact on our mental and emotional well-being. Exercise releases endorphins, which are natural mood boosters, and helps reduce stress and anxiety. When we prioritize our fitness, we are better equipped to handle the challenges and demands of our careers and relationships.

1

Spirituality, regardless of religious affiliation, pl ays a si gnificant rol e in nourish- ing the whole self. It provides a sense of purpose, meaning, and connection to something greater than ourselves. Engaging in spiritual practices such as medi- tation, mindfulness, or connecting with nature can help reduce stress, enhance self-awareness, and promote inner peace. This, in turn, can positively influence our relationships, careers, and overall well-being.

The Impact of Diet on Overall Well-being

ONE CRUCIAL ASPECT that connects relationships, careers, fitness, and spirituality is our diet. The food we consume has a direct impact on our physical, mental, and emotional health. It provides the necessary nutrients for our bodies to function optimally and affects o ur e nergy l evels, mood, a nd c ognitive abilities.

When we nourish our bodies with a balanced and nutritious diet, we provide the fuel needed for physical performance, mental clarity, and emotional well-being. Certain foods are known to have specific b enefits fo r ou r ov erall he alth. For example, foods rich in omega-3 fatty acids, such as fatty fish, w alnuts, and flaxseeds, have b een l inked to improved mood a nd reduced r isk of depression. Similarly, foods high in antioxidants, such as berries, dark chocolate, and leafy greens, can help protect our brain cells and improve cognitive function.

Moreover, a healthy diet can positively impact our relationships, careers, fitness, and spirituality. When we prioritize our nutrition, we have more energy and vitality to engage in meaningful relationships, excel in our careers, and pursue our fitness g oals. It also enhances o ur a bility to c onnect with o ur s pirituality, as we are more attuned to our bodies and minds.

The Purpose of the Book

THE PURPOSE OF THIS book, "Nurturing Wholeness with Primary Food for Balanced Living" is to provide a comprehensive guide to understanding and nurturing the interconnectedness of these four dimensions. By exploring the importance of healthy relationships, fulfilling careers, effective fitness routines, and meaningful spiritual practices, readers will gain insights and practical strategies to create a balanced and vibrant lifestyle.

Throughout the book, we will delve into various topics, including building healthy connections, effective communication, conflict resolution, finding meaning and purpose in our work, setting goals, designing exercise routines, nutrition, mindfulness, exploring different spiritual practices, and developing healthy habits and routines. By integrating these aspects into our lives, we can create a harmonious and fulfilling existence that nourishes our whole selves.

Through the exploration of the interconnectedness of relationships, careers, fitness, and spirituality, and the impact of diet on overall well-being, this book aims to empower readers to take charge of their lives and cultivate vibrant and

2

fulfilling experiences. By understanding and nurturing the whole self, we can create a ripple effect of positivity and well-being that extends beyond ourselves, impacting our relationships, careers, communities, and the world at large.

In our daily lives, we often separate different aspects of ourselves – our personal relationships, careers, fitness routines, and spiritual practices. However, these four areas are actually deeply interconnected and have a significant impact on each other. When one aspect is neglected or struggling, it can have a ripple effect on our overall well-being and happiness.

Firstly, our relationships with others play a crucial role in our overall health and happiness. The bonds we form with friends, family, and partners can provide us with a sense of support, belonging, and love. Studies have shown that positive relationships can lead to a longer life, decreased stress levels, and increased resilience in the face of challenges. On the other hand, toxic or strained relationships can have detrimental effects on our mental and emotional well- being, as well as physical health. It is essential to nurture and cultivate healthy relationships in order to have a strong foundation for a fulfilling life.

Our careers also have a significant impact on our overall well-being. Many of us spend a large portion of our lives working, and our jobs can greatly influence our happiness and sense of purpose. Finding a career that aligns with our values and provides a sense of meaning and fulfillment can greatly contribute to our overall well-being. However, a negative or unfulfilling job can lead to chronic stress, burnout, and negative impacts on our mental and physical health. It is important to prioritize finding a career that allows us to thrive and supports our overall well-being.

In addition to our external relationships and careers, our bodies also require attention and care through fitness and exercise. Physical fitness not only benefits our overall health, but it also has significant effects on our mental health. Regular exercise has been shown to reduce symptoms of depression, anxiety, and stress, and can also improve sleep and cognitive function. On the other hand, a sedentary lifestyle can have negative effects on our mental and physical well-being, leading to fatigue, decreased energy, and decreased overall strength and mobility.

Finally, our spiritual practices also have a significant impact on our well-being. This can include connecting with nature, practicing mindfulness and meditation, and exploring different belief systems. These practices can provide us with a sense of inner peace, purpose, and connection to something greater than ourselves. Research has shown that those who have a regular spiritual practice have better overall mental and emotional health, as well as increased resilience and a sense of purpose and fulfillment in life.

So how do these four aspects – relationships, careers, fitness, and spirituality – all tie together when it comes to our diets and overall lifestyle? Our diet, or the foods we eat on a regular basis, is fuel for our bodies and can greatly impact our physical, mental, and emotional well-being. When we prioritize taking care of our relationships, careers, fitness routines, and spiritual practices, we also prioritize prioritizing our diet and how it supports our overall well-being.

For example, having a strong support system through our relationships can influence our food choices. When we feel fulfilled and supported in our personal connections, we may be less likely to turn to unhealthy comfort foods as a coping mechanism for emotional stress. This in turn can have positive effects on our physical health.

Similarly, having a fulfilling career can also impact our diet. When we are stressed or unhappy at work, we may turn to unhealthy foods for comfort or as a quick fix. However, when we find meaning and purpose in our work, we may be more likely to prioritize and make time for cooking healthy meals and prioritizing our overall well-being.

Regular exercise is also closely tied to our diet. Physical activity helps regulate our appetite and can also influence our food choices. Engaging in regular exercise can also increase our motivation and discipline, making us more likely to make healthier food choices and stick to a balanced diet.

Finally, our spiritual practices can also play a role in our diet. Practicing mindfulness and connecting with our inner selves can help us become more aware of our body's needs and listen to its cues for hunger and fullness. This can help us make healthier food choices and develop a more mindful and balanced approach to our diets.

In summary, our relationships, careers, fitness routines, and spiritual practices all have a profound impact on our overall well-being, and our diet is tightly interconnected with each of these aspects. When we nourish our whole selves by prioritizing these areas and maintaining a balanced and healthy lifestyle, we can experience the full benefits of each individual aspect, leading to a vibrant and fulfilling life.

The food we consume has a direct impact on our mental, emotional, and physical well-being. It is not just about eating to satisfy our hunger; rather, it is about fueling our bodies with the necessary nutrients to function at its best. Just like a car needs fuel to run efficiently, our bodies need the right kinds of food to perform optimally.

Our diet not only affects our physical health but also plays a significant role in our emotional and mental well-being. Studies have shown that certain nutrients and foods can help improve mood, cognitive function, and even reduce symptoms of anxiety and depression. On the other hand, a diet high in processed and unhealthy foods can lead to a decline in mental health and overall well-being.

Let's take a closer look at how our diet impacts the different aspects of our lives:

Emotional Well-being

OUR EMOTIONS CAN BE influenced by the food we consume. A study published in the American Journal of Clinical Nutrition found that individuals who consume fast food and processed foods are more likely to experience symptoms of depression compared to those who follow a healthier diet. These foods are often high in unhealthy fats, sugar, and additives, which can negatively affect our mood and energy levels.

On the other hand, certain foods have been linked to boosting our mood and overall emotional well-being. Foods rich in omega-3 fatty acids, such as salmon, tuna, and walnuts, have been shown to reduce symptoms of depression and improve mood. Fruits and vegetables, especially those rich in antioxidants, can also have a positive impact on our emotional health.

Mental Clarity and Cognitive Function

OUR BRAIN NEEDS FUEL to function effectively and consistently. Just like any other organ in our bodies, the brain relies on the nutrients we consume to keep it functioning optimally. Foods high in omega-3 fatty acids, such as fish, can help improve cognitive function and protect against age-related cognitive decline.

Additionally, studies have shown a strong link between nutrition and our ability to learn and retain information. A diet rich in fruits, vegetables, and whole grains can support the brain's function and promote better memory and concentration.

Physical Performance

IT'S NO SECRET THAT a healthy diet is essential for physical performance. Whether you're an athlete or someone who enjoys exercising regularly, the food you consume is crucial for fueling your body and aiding in physical recovery. For example, consuming protein-rich foods can help build and repair muscles, while carbohydrates provide energy for physical activity and replace glycogen stores.

Moreover, certain foods and nutrients can also help improve endurance, reduce muscle soreness, and speed up recovery time. For instance, consuming tart cherry juice has been shown to reduce muscle soreness and inflammation, thus improving physical performance.

Overall Health and Well-being

OUR DIET NOT ONLY IMPACTS our emotional, mental, and physical health, but it also plays a role in our overall well-being. Following a healthy and balanced diet has been linked to a reduced risk of chronic diseases such as heart disease, diabetes, and obesity. Consuming a variety of whole, nutrient-dense foods can also boost our immune system and protect against illnesses.

On the other hand, a diet high in processed and unhealthy foods can lead to weight gain, inflammation, and an increased risk of chronic diseases. Moreover, these types of foods often lack the necessary nutrients for our bodies to function and can leave us feeling fatigued and sluggish.

As you can see, our diet plays a vital role in our overall well-being, including our emotional, mental, and physical health. Therefore, it is essential to make conscious and informed choices when it comes to the food we consume.

Some tips for incorporating healthy eating habits into your daily routine include:

- Eating a variety of fruits, vegetables, lean proteins, whole grains, and healthy fats.

- Limiting processed and high-sugar foods as much as possible.

- Being mindful of portion sizes.

- Meal planning and preparation to ensure a balanced diet.

- Staying hydrated by drinking enough water throughout the day.

In the next chapters, we will explore the different types of foods that c an help enhance our emotional, mental, and physical well-being. We will also discuss the importance of a balanced and varied diet and how to incorporate healthier food choices into our lifestyles.

By understanding the impact of diet on our overall well-being, we can make conscious decisions to nourish our bodies, minds, and souls. Remember, food is more than just fuel; it is an essential part of our well-being. So, let's make the right choices to nurture and nourish our whole selves.

1.4 The Purpose of the Book

THE PURPOSE OF THIS book, "Nurturing Wholeness with Primary Food for Balanced Living" is to explore the inter-connectedness of these four key aspects of our lives and how they contribute to our overall well-being. By understanding the importance of healthy relationships, fulfilling careers, effective fitness routines, and meaningful spirituality practices, we can create a balanced and vibrant lifestyle.

In today's fast-paced and interconnected world, it is easy to overlook the impact that these different areas of our lives have on each other. However, by recognizing their interconnectedness, we can begin to see how they influence and shape our overall health and happiness.

First and foremost, healthy relationships are essential for our well-being. They provide us with emotional support, love, and a sense of belonging. When our relationships are thriving, we experience greater happiness, reduced stress levels, and improved mental health. In this book, we will explore strategies for building healthy connections, effective communication, conflict resolution, and cultivating supportive relationships.

Our careers also play a significant role in our overall well-being. When we find meaning and purpose in our work, we experience a sense of fulfillment and satisfaction. However, if our careers are unfulfilling or cause excessive stress, it can negatively impact our mental and physical health. In this book, we will delve into finding meaning and purpose in our work, setting goals, managing time effectively, and achieving work-life balance.

Physical fitness is another crucial aspect of our well-being. Regular exercise not only improves our physical health but also has a profound impact on our mental and emotional well-being. It reduces stress, boosts mood, improves sleep, and increases overall energy levels. In this book, we will explore the importance of physical fitness, designing effective exercise routines, and adopting healthy eating habits to fuel our bodies.

Spirituality, regardless of religious affiliation, provides a sense of connection to something greater than ourselves. It helps us find inner peace, purpose, and meaning in life. Engaging in spiritual practices such as meditation, mindfulness, and connecting with nature can have a profound impact on our overall well-being. In this book, we will explore different spiritual practices and how they can enhance our lives.

While these four aspects of our lives are essential, it is important to recognize that they are not isolated from each other. They are interconnected and influence one another. For example, the quality of our relationships can impact our career satisfaction, and our physical fitness can affect our spiritual well-being. By understanding these connections, we can create a more holistic approach to our overall well-being.

In addition to exploring the interconnectedness of relationships, careers, fitness, and spirituality, this book will also delve into the impact of diet on our overall well-being. The foods we consume have a direct influence on our emotional, mental, and physical health. Certain nutrients can improve emotional well-being, enhance mental clarity, and fuel our bodies for optimal physical performance. In this book, we will explore the relationship between food and health, nutrients for emotional well-being, foods for mental clarity, and fueling the body for physical performance.

The purpose of this book is to provide you with practical strategies, insights, and knowledge to help you cultivate a vibrant and balanced life. By nourishing the whole self through relationships, careers, fitness, spirituality, and diet, you can experience greater happiness, fulfillment, and overall well-being. This book aims to empower you to make positive changes in your life and embrace a holistic approach to self-care.

Through the exploration of these interconnected aspects, you will gain a deeper understanding of how they contribute to your overall well-being. By implementing the strategies and practices outlined in this book, you can create a more balanced and fulfilling life. Embracing the journey of nourishing the whole self will not only benefit you but also have a ripple effect on those around you, creating a positive impact on your relationships, career, and community.

In conclusion, the purpose of this book is to guide you on a journey of self-discovery and empowerment. By understanding the interconnectedness of rela- tionships, careers, fitness, spirituality, and diet, you can cultivate a vibrant and balanced life. Through practical strategies and insights, you will be equipped to make positive changes and embrace a holistic approach to self-care. Let us embark on this transformative journey together and create a ripple effect of well-being and fulfillment in our lives and the lives of those around us.

Nurturing Relationships

O ur relationships with others play a crucial role in our overall well-being. Whether it's with romantic partners, friends, family, or colleagues, the quality of our connections can greatly impact our physical, emotional, and mental health. In this section, we will explore the importance of building and maintaining healthy relationships and how it contributes to nourishing the whole self.

The Importance of Healthy Relationships

HUMANS ARE SOCIAL CREATURES, and we thrive on connection and belonging. Positive relationships provide us with emotional support, reduce stress, and help us feel more fulfilled in life. On the other hand, unhealthy relationships can have detrimental effects on our well-being, causing stress, anxiety, and even physical health problems. It's essential to understand the role of relationships in our lives and ensure that we have healthy and supportive connections.

Communication and Emotional Intelligence

ONE OF THE KEY ASPECTS of maintaining healthy relationships is effective com- munication. It's the foundation of all types of relationships, and without it, misunderstandings and conflicts can arise. Good communication involves active listening, expressing oneself clearly and honestly, and being aware of non-verbal cues. It also means being able to resolve conflicts and handle difficult emotions in a productive and respectful manner.

Emotional intelligence, or the ability to understand and manage one's emotions and the emotions of others, is also crucial in building healthy connections. It allows individuals to better navigate their relationships, respond to difficult situations with empathy and compassion, and promote mutual understanding and support.

Conflict Resolution and Boundaries

NO RELATIONSHIP IS perfect, and conflicts are bound to happen. However, it's how we handle conflicts that determine whether our relationships will suffer or thrive. Healthy relationships require effective conflict resolution, where both parties communicate openly and respectfully, listen to each other's perspectives, and work together to reach a solution. Learning to establish and respect personal boundaries is also vital for maintaining healthy relationships. Boundaries ensure that our needs, values, and limits are respected, and that we're not compromising our well-being for the sake of others.

Cultivating Supportive Relationships

THERE'S A SAYING THAT goes, "you are the average of the five people you spend the most time with." Our relationships can shape our habits, perspective, and ultimately, our well-being. It's essential to surround ourselves with people who support and uplift us, rather than bring us down. These supportive relationships can give us a greater sense of purpose and motivation, as well as provide us with a support system during challenging times.

Now that we've explored the importance of having healthy relationships let's delve deeper into how they contribute to nourishing the whole self.

Emotional Health Healthy relationships can provide us with emotional support, understanding, and validation. When we feel loved and accepted by the people in our lives, we're more likely to have a positive outlook on life, feel less stressed, and have better self-esteem. On the other hand, unhealthy relationships can have adverse effects on our emotional well-being, causing feelings of worthlessness, loneliness, and even depression.

Mental Health Our relationships also play a significant role in our mental health. Healthy connections can help us build resilience and cope better with life's challenges. They provide us with a safe space to express our thoughts and feelings, seek advice and support, and feel a sense of belonging. On the contrary, toxic relationships can be a source of stress and anxiety, which can lead to mental health issues if left unaddressed.

Physical Health The impact of our relationships on our physical health may not be as obvious, but it's just as crucial. Studies have shown that individuals in stable, supportive relationships tend to have better physical health, including lower blood pressure, reduced risk of heart disease, and improved immune function. On the other hand, unhealthy relationships can lead to increased stress levels, which can negatively affect our immune system and overall health.

Spiritual Well-being Healthy relationships can also contribute to our spiritual well-being. When we feel connected and supported by our loved ones, we often experience a sense of peace and purpose. Our relationships can also help us through our spiritual journeys by providing us with a community that shares our beliefs and values. And for those without a specific religious or spiritual practice, having meaningful relationships can fill the void and provide a sense of fulfillment and connectedness.

In conclusion, building and nurturing healthy relationships is crucial in nourishing the whole self. It's not only about surrounding ourselves with people who make us happy, but also about learning to communicate effectively, manage our emotions, and set boundaries. Healthy relationships can contribute to our emotional, mental, physical, and spiritual well-being, ultimately helping us lead more vibrant and fulfilling lives.

When it comes to fostering healthy relationships, communication and emotional intelligence play crucial roles. Effective communication allows for better un- derstanding and connection with others, while emotional intelligence helps us navigate our own and others' emotions in a productive manner.

The Importance of Communication in Relationships

COMMUNICATION IS THE foundation of any relationship, whether it be romantic, familial, or platonic. It is the way we express our thoughts, feelings, and needs to others. Without good communication, misunderstandings and conflicts can arise, leading to a breakdown in the relationship.

In order to have healthy relationships, it is important to communicate openly and effectively. This means actively listening to the other person, expressing oneself clearly and respectfully, and being open to compromise and understanding. Good communication can also help build trust and deepen the connection between individuals.

Emotional Intelligence and its Role in Relationships

EMOTIONAL INTELLIGENCE refers to our ability to recognize, understand, and manage our own emotions, as well as the emotions of others. It is a key component in building and maintaining healthy relationships.

Having emotional intelligence allows us to better understand and empathize with others, communicate effectively, and manage conflicts in a constructive way. It also helps us regulate our own emotions, preventing us from reacting impulsively and causing harm to our relationships.

Cultivating Emotional Intelligence

EMOTIONAL INTELLIGENCE is not something we are born with, but rather a skill that can be developed and strengthened over time. Here are some tips for cultivating emotional intelligence in relationships:

- Practice self-awareness: Pay attention to your own emotions and how they affect your thoughts and actions. Understanding your own feelings can help you better understand and relate to the feelings of others.

- Practice active listening: This means truly listening to the other person without interrupting or judging. Pay attention not only to their words, but also to their body language and tone of voice.

• Validate others' emotions: When someone shares their emotions with you, acknowledge and validate them. This doesn't mean you have to agree with them, but rather show them that you understand and empathize with their perspective.

• Use "I" statements: When expressing your own emotions and needs, use "I" statements to avoid blaming or accusing the other person. For example, instead of saying "You always make me mad when you don't listen," try saying "I feel frustrated when I don't feel heard."

• Practice empathy: Put yourself in others' shoes and try to understand their perspectives and emotions. This can help strengthen your connection and avoid conflicts.

• Communicate your boundaries: It's important to communicate your bound- aries and limits in a compassionate and respectful manner. This can help prevent misunderstandings and conflicts in the future.

• Take responsibility for your actions: Part of emotional intelligence is being able to take responsibility for our words and actions. If you make a mistake, own up to it and apologize sincerely.

Conflict Resolution and Emotional Intelligence

CONFLICTS ARE A NATURAL part of any relationship. However, how we handle conflicts can make or break a relationship. Emotional intelligence plays a significant role in resolving conflicts in a healthy and productive way.

When conflicts arise, it is important to stay calm and avoid reacting impulsively. Take a step back, assess the situation, and try to understand the other person's perspective. Use your emotional intelligence skills to empathize and communicate effectively, rather than resorting to blaming or manipulation tactics.

It's also important to be open to compromise and respectful communication, rather than seeking to win or be right. By approaching conflicts with emo- tional intelligence, we can often find a resolution that satisfies both parties and strengthens the relationship.

The Role of Communication and Emotional Intelligence in Nourishing the Whole Self

OUR RELATIONSHIPS ARE a significant part of our lives, and they greatly impact our overall well-being. By cultivating effective communication and emotional intelligence in our relationships, we can nourish not only our connections with others, but also our own mental, emotional, and even physical health.

In addition, these skills can also aid in balancing the other aspects of our lives, such as our careers, fitness, and spirituality. By understanding and managing our own emotions and effectively communicating with others, we can create a more fulfilling and balanced life.

In conclusion, communication and emotional intelligence are key factors in nurturing and sustaining healthy and meaningful relationships. By focusing on developing and strengthening these skills, we can foster deeper connections, resolve conflicts in a healthy manner, and ultimately nourish the whole self. So, let's make an effort to communicate openly and empathetically, and to constantly work on our emotional intelligence for the benefit of ourselves and our relationships.

Healthy relationships require effective communication and the ability to resolve conflicts peacefully. However, many people struggle with handling conflicts and setting appropriate boundaries, which can lead to strained relationships and negative effects on overall well-being.

Understanding Conflict Resolution

CONFLICT IS A NATURAL part of any relationship. It occurs when there is a disagree- ment or clash of opinions between individuals. Conflicts can arise in romantic relationships, friendships, family dynamics, and even in the workplace. How conflicts are handled can greatly impact the health of the relationship.

Conflict resolution is the process of finding a peaceful and mutually satisfactory resolution to a disagreement. Instead of trying to avoid or ignore conflicts, it is important to address and resolve them in a healthy manner. This involves effective communication, active listening, and a willingness to understand and respect the other person's perspective.

Communication and Active Listening

EFFECTIVE COMMUNICATION is the key to resolving conflicts and building healthy relationships. It involves expressing thoughts and feelings clearly and listening actively to the other person's viewpoint.

When conflicts arise, it is important to avoid blaming and criticizing the other person. Instead, use "I" statements to express your feelings and avoid attacking the other person. for example, instead of saying "you never do the dishes," try saying "I feel overwhelmed when the dishes pile up." This approach can help to avoid defensiveness and create a more constructive conversation.

Active listening, on the other hand, involves fully paying attention to the other person's words, tone, and body language. It is essential to listen without interrupting or judging, and to ask clarifying questions to ensure understanding. This helps to promote empathy, understanding, and effective communication.

Setting Boundaries

BOUNDARIES ARE A CRUCIAL aspect of healthy relationships. They are the limits and guidelines we set for ourselves and others in order to protect our physical, emotional, and mental well-being. Setting boundaries can help to prevent conflict and maintain a sense of self-respect.

It is important to communicate your boundaries clearly and assertively. State what you are comfortable with and what you believe is necessary for the health of the relationship. For example, if you feel that your partner should not yell at you during an argument, communicate that calmly and firmly. Remember that it is also important to respect the boundaries of others, and be willing to compromise and find solutions that work for both parties.

Cultivating Supportive Relationships

HEALTHY RELATIONSHIPS involve mutual support, respect, and understanding. It is important to surround yourself with people who uplift and support you, and who you can do the same for in return.

When conflicts arise, it can be helpful to seek support from friends, family, or a therapist. Talking to someone neutral can provide new perspectives and help to diffuse tension. Additionally, having a supportive network can provide a sense of validation and help to cope with any negative emotions that may arise from conflicts.

The Impact of Healthy Relationships on Overall Well-being

HAVING HEALTHY RELATIONSHIPS not only benefits our emotional and mental health, but also has a positive impact on our physical well-being. Studies have shown that people in supportive and satisfying relationships have lower rates of stress, anxiety, and depression. They also have better immune systems and live longer.

On the other hand, unhealthy or toxic relationships can have detrimental effects on our overall well-being. Constant conflict and stress can lead to physical ailments such as headaches, digestive issues, and even heart disease. It is important to recognize when a relationship is having a negative impact and to actively work towards resolving conflicts or letting go of toxic relationships.

The Role of Boundaries in Self-care

OFTEN, SETTING BOUNDARIES can feel uncomfortable or even selfish. But it is important to remember that boundaries are a form of self-care. They help us maintain our sense of self-worth and protect us from emotional harm.

By setting and enforcing boundaries, we are showing ourselves love and respect, and in turn, teaching others to treat us with the same level of care and respect. Without boundaries, we may find ourselves constantly giving and sacrificing, which can lead to burnout and resentment in our relationships.

Conclusion

IN ORDER TO CULTIVATE and maintain healthy relationships, it is important to understand and practice effective conflict resolution and setting boundaries.

These skills not only help to resolve conflicts peacefully, but also contribute to our overall well-being.

By communicating effectively, actively listening, setting boundaries, and sur- rounding ourselves with supportive relationships, we can nurture and nourish our whole selves. This includes our emotional, mental, and physical well-being, and leads to a more fulfilling and vibrant life.

In the previous sections, we discussed the importance of building and main- taining healthy relationships. But sometimes, we may find ourselves in toxic or unsupportive relationships that drain our energy and hinder our personal growth.

It's essential to cultivate supportive relationships in our lives because they can provide us with the necessary support, encouragement, and love that we need to thrive. These relationships can be with our family, friends, colleagues, mentors, or even our pets.

So how do we cultivate supportive relationships? First, we must identify the qualities that make a relationship supportive. These qualities include trust, respect, open communication, and a sense of reciprocity. Supportive relationships are built on a strong foundation of mutual understanding and care.

Here are some tips on how to cultivate supportive relationships:

1. Be there for each other: A supportive relationship means that both parties show up for each other, regardless of the circumstances. It's essential to be present and available for your loved ones when they need you, whether it's through physical presence or emotional support.

2. Communicate effectively: Open and honest communication is crucial in any relationship. It's essential to express your thoughts and feelings clearly and listen to your partner without judgment. Effective communication helps build trust and strengthens the bond between individuals.

3. Show appreciation and gratitude: In supportive relationships, it's essential to express gratitude and appreciation for each other. A simple "thank you" can go a long way in making someone feel valued and loved. Take the time to acknowledge the little things that your partner does for you and let them know how much you appreciate them.

4. Respect boundaries: Boundaries are essential in any relationship, and they should be respected to maintain a healthy dynamic. It's crucial to communicate and establish boundaries in a supportive relationship to ensure that both parties feel respected and heard.

5. Be a good listener: In supportive relationships, it's not just about talking; listening is just as important. Be present and attentive when your partner is sharing their thoughts and feelings with you. Avoid interrupting or trying to solve their problems. Sometimes, all they need is someone to listen and understand.

1. Offer support and encouragement: Supportive relationships involve cheering each other on and providing encouragement. It's crucial to be there for your partner during their highs and lows, offering motivation and support in achieving their goals and dreams.

2. Practice empathy and understanding: In any relationship, it's essential to have empathy and understanding towards your partner. Put yourself in their shoes and try to see things from their perspective. This can help strengthen the connection and foster a deeper understanding of one another.

3. Celebrate each other's successes: In a supportive relationship, it's important to celebrate each other's achievements and successes. Whether big or small, it's vital to recognize and acknowledge your partner's victories and show them that you are proud of them.

4. Share vulnerability and be authentic: Vulnerability and authenticity are the foundations of a supportive relationship. It's crucial to create a safe space where you and your partner can open up and be your true selves. By sharing your vulnerabilities, you build a stronger connection and deepen your bond with your partner.

5. Keep a positive outlook: A positive attitude can go a long way in creating and maintaining a supportive relationship. Focus on the good things in your relationship and be grateful for each other. By keeping a positive outlook, you can overcome any challenges that may arise and continue to cultivate a supportive and loving connection.

In summary, supportive relationships are crucial for our overall well-being and personal growth. By cultivating these relationships and nurturing them with love, care, and understanding, we can create a strong support system that helps us thrive in all areas of our lives. Remember, it's not about the number of relationships we have, but the quality of those relationships that truly matter. So let's prioritize cultivating supportive relationships and watch how they positively impact our diets and lifestyles.

Thriving in Your Career

As humans, we spend a significant amount of our time and energy on our careers. It is often one of the first questions we ask when meeting someone new: "What do you do for a living?" Our careers contribute to our sense of identity and provide us with financial stability, but they can also have a profound impact on our overall well-being.

Many people struggle to find meaning and purpose in their work, which can lead to feelings of dissatisfaction, burnout, and even mental health issues. It is crucial to understand the importance of finding fulfillment in our careers and how it can positively impact our lives.

The Connection Between Career and Overall Well-being

WHILE DISCUSSING THE different aspects of our lives, it is essential to recognize how interconnected they are. Our careers do not just affect our financial stability but also impact our relationships, physical health, and spirituality.

Studies have shown that job satisfaction is closely linked to overall life satisfaction. When we are unhappy in our careers, it can affect our relationships, causing tension, and even lead to arguments. It can also impact our physical health, whether it is through stress-related illnesses or an unhealthy work-life balance that leaves little time for exercise and self-care. And for some, their careers can become all-consuming, leaving little time or energy for spiritual practices and personal growth.

On the other hand, when we find meaning and purpose in our work, it can positively impact every aspect of our lives. It can improve our relationships as we are happier and more fulfilled, leading to stronger connections with others. It can also increase our motivation to take care of our physical health, leading to better overall well-being. And for some, their careers can align with their spiritual values and beliefs, providing an opportunity for personal growth and fulfillment.

Thus, understanding the connection between our careers and our overall well- being is essential in finding balance and living a vibrant life.

Finding Meaning and Purpose in Your Career

THE IDEA OF FINDING meaning and purpose in your career may seem daunting, but it is entirely achievable. Here are some steps to help guide you in this process:

1. Reflect on Your Personal Values and Interests Start by reflecting on your personal values and interests. What is important to you? What are you passionate about? Understanding your values and interests can help guide you towards a career that aligns with them.

Make a list of your top values and interests, and use them as a filter when exploring career options. This exercise will give you a better understanding of what you are looking for in a career and help narrow down your options.

2. Identify Your Strengths and Skills Another crucial step in finding purpose in your work is to identify your strengths and skills. When we are doing work that aligns with our strengths, we are more likely to feel engaged and fulfilled. Take some time to reflect on your strengths and skills, and consider how they can be applied to different careers.

If you are struggling to identify your strengths and skills, ask for feedback from friends, family, or colleagues. Others may be able to see strengths in us that we are not aware of.

3. Explore Different Career Options Once you have a good understanding of your values, interests, strengths, and skills, it is time to explore different career options. Take the time to research different industries, job roles, and companies that align with your values and interests. Consider reaching out to people currently working in these areas to learn more about their experiences and gain insights into potential career paths.

Keep an open mind during this exploration process and be open to trying new things. You may discover a career path that you never considered before but turns out to be a perfect fit for you.

4. Set Meaningful Goals As you explore different career options, it is essential to set meaningful goals for yourself. What do you want to achieve in your career? How do you define success for yourself? Setting achievable goals can give you direction and motivation in your career path.

Be sure to make your goals specific and measurable so that you can track your progress. Also, consider breaking down your goals into smaller, manageable steps, making them less overwhelming and more attainable.

5. Continuously Learn and Grow Lastly, remember that learning and growth are essential for finding meaning and purpose in your work. Never stop learning and challenging yourself to grow both personally and professionally. This continuous development can lead to new opportunities and help you stay motivated and fulfilled in your career.

Work-Life Balance and Stress Management

IN THE FAST-PACED MODERN world, it can be challenging to find a balance between our work and personal lives. However, it is crucial to prioritize work-life balance and stress management to avoid burnout and maintain our overall well-being.

Here are some tips for balancing your career and personal life:

• Set boundaries: Make a clear distinction between work time and personal time. Set boundaries with your work responsibilities to allow yourself time for rest and relaxation.

• Prioritize self-care: Make sure to schedule time for self-care activities, such as exercise, hobbies, and spending time with loved ones. Put these activities on your calendar and treat them as essential appointments.

• Utilize your support system: Lean on your support system, whether it is friends, family, or a therapist, for help and guidance during challenging times.

• Develop stress management techniques: Find healthy ways to cope with stress, such as practicing mindfulness, going for a walk, or engaging in a hobby.

Remember that achieving balance and managing stress looks different for every- one, so find what works best for you and prioritize it.

Final Thoughts

FINDING MEANING AND purpose in our careers is an ongoing process that requires self-reflection, exploration, and continuous growth. When we take the time to align our work with our values and interests, it can have a profound impact on our overall well-being.

Remember to prioritize work-life balance and stress management, and continue to grow and learn in your career to sustain a fulfilling and vibrant life.

In today's fast-paced world, it can be easy to feel overwhelmed and constantly behind schedule. This is where setting goals and managing time effectively becomes crucial. By having a clear understanding of what we want to accomplish and implementing effective time management techniques, we can achieve our goals and create a more balanced and fulfilling life.

The Importance of Setting Goals

GOAL SETTING IS THE process of identifying what we want to achieve and creating a plan to reach those objectives. Without clear goals, we may lack direction and feel like we are spinning our wheels without making any progress. Setting goals allows us to focus our efforts and channel our energy towards meaningful and fulfilling pursuits.

When setting goals, it is important to make them specific, measurable, attainable, relevant, and time-bound (SMART). This means that our goals should be clearly defined, have a way to track progress, be realistically achievable, align with our values and overall life plan, and have a deadline to work towards.

Identifying Priorities

ONE OF THE FIRST STEPS in effective time management is identifying our priorities. This means recognizing what is most important to us and making it a priority in our daily lives. This could be spending time with loved ones, working towards a career goal, or dedicating time to fitness and self-care. By understanding our priorities, we can structure our days and allocate our time accordingly.

To help identify priorities, it can be helpful to make a list of our current obligations and responsibilities, both personal and professional. From there, we can evaluate which tasks align with our priorities and which ones can be delegated or eliminated.

Time Management Strategies

ONCE WE HAVE A CLEAR understanding of our priorities, we can implement time management strategies to make the most of our days. Some effective techniques include:

• Creating a schedule or to-do list: By mapping out our tasks and appoint- ments in a visual format, we can have a clearer picture of our day and avoid missing important deadlines or appointments.

• Utilizing the Pomodoro Technique: This time management method involves breaking our work into 25-minute intervals, followed by a short break. This can help increase focus and productivity.

• Setting boundaries: It is important to set boundaries and learn to say no to tasks or commitments that do not align with our priorities. This allows us to protect our time and energy for what truly matters to us.

• Maximizing efficiency: Multitasking may seem like a productive approach, but it can actually decrease efficiency and result in low-quality work. Instead, focus on one task at a time and give it your full attention.

• Taking breaks: It may seem counterintuitive, but taking short breaks throughout the day can help boost productivity and prevent burnout.

Adjusting and Re-evaluating

AS WE WORK TOWARDS our goals and navigate through our daily responsibilities, it is important to regularly re-evaluate our priorities and time management strategies. Sometimes we may need to adjust our schedule or change our approach to better align with our current needs and goals.

It is also important to give ourselves grace and recognize that we are not always going to get everything done perfectly. Balancing relationships, career, fitness, and spirituality can be a constant juggling act, and it is okay to make mistakes or have days where we feel off track. The key is to keep moving forward and remain flexible to adjust as needed.

The Relationship Between Time Management and Diet

EFFECTIVE TIME MANAGEMENT not only helps us achieve our goals and create a more balanced life, but it can also have a positive impact on our diet. By prioritizing tasks and managing our time effectively, we can avoid skipping meals or relying on fast food options. Planning and preparing healthy meals in advance can also save time and make it easier to stick to a nutritious diet.

Additionally, incorporating mindful eating practices into our routine can help us make mindful food choices and tune in to our body's needs. By taking the time to enjoy our meals and staying present in the moment, we can better nourish our bodies and form a healthier relationship with food.

Conclusion

SETTING GOALS AND MANAGING time effectively are crucial components of creating a vibrant and fulfilling life. By understanding our priorities, implementing time management strategies, and regularly re-evaluating our approach, we can achieve our goals and maintain a balanced lifestyle. This not only benefits our personal well-being but also positively impacts our diet and overall health. Remember, finding balance is a continuous journey, and with determination and perseverance, we can achieve it.

Learning is a lifelong journey, and it is essential to continuously develop and improve our skills. In today's fast-paced and constantly changing world, staying stagnant and not learning new things can hinder our growth and success. De- veloping skills and engaging in continuous learning can not only enhance our careers but also contribute to our overall well-being.

The Importance of Developing Skills and Continuous Learning

DEVELOPING SKILLS AND engaging in continuous learning is vital for many reasons. Firstly, it helps us stay competitive in our careers. In today's job market, employers value individuals who are continuously improving and learning new skills. By developing our skills and staying updated with industry trends and advancements, we can increase our value and chances for career progression.

Continuous learning also allows us to adapt to changing situations and challenges. The world is constantly evolving, and new technologies and processes are always emerging. By continuously learning, we can stay updated and adapt to these changes more efficiently. This adaptability also helps us to be more resilient and navigate through difficult times.

Moreover, learning new skills and expanding our knowledge can bring a sense of purpose and fulfillment. By setting goals for our learning journey and achieving them, we gain a sense of accomplishment. This can boost our self-esteem and motivation, leading to a more fulfilling and satisfying life.

Ways to Develop Skills and Engage in Continuous

Learning

DEVELOPING SKILLS AND engaging in continuous learning does not always have to be a formal process. There are various ways to improve our skills and expand our knowledge outside of the traditional classroom setting. Here are some suggestions:

- Attend workshops, seminars, or conferences related to your field of inter- est. These events provide opportunities for networking and learning from industry experts.

- Take online courses or certifications. Many reputable organizations of- fer online courses that allow individuals to learn at their own pace and convenience.

- Read books, articles, or blogs about topics that interest you. This not only helps to expand your knowledge but also improves your reading and critical thinking skills.

- Join professional organizations or groups. These groups provide networking opportunities, resources, and even mentorship programs that can help in developing your skills.

- Volunteer or take on new tasks or projects at work. This can expose you to new challenges and allow you to learn new skills, making you more valuable to your organization.

Developing Different Types of Skills

WHEN IT COMES TO DEVELOPING skills, there are various types that we can focus on. The specific skills we choose to develop will depend on our career goals, personal interests, and areas where we feel we may be lacking. Here are some examples of different types of skills that we can develop and their benefits:

- Technical skills: These are job-specific skills that are necessary for a particular job or industry. Developing technical skills can increase our value and effectiveness in our current roles and make us more marketable in the job market.

- Soft skills: These are non-technical skills such as leadership, communication, and time management. These skills are essential for career growth and success, as they improve our relationships with others, help us manage our time effectively, and make us more efficient in our work.

- Personal development skills: These are skills that help us improve as individuals, such as self-awareness, emotional intelligence, and adaptability. Developing these skills can lead to personal growth and self-improvement, leading to a more fulfilling and satisfying life.

Utilizing Feedback and Self-Reflection

PART OF DEVELOPING skills and engaging in continuous learning involves receiving feedback and reflecting on our progress. Feedback provides us with valuable insights and helps us identify areas where we can improve. We can receive feedback from colleagues, mentors, or even through self-assessment.

Self-reflection is also crucial in the learning process. Taking the time to reflect on our progress, strengths, and weaknesses can help us identify areas we need to work on and make effective plans for improvement. Self-reflection also helps us stay focused and motivated in our learning journey.

Incorporating Continuous Learning into Our Daily Lives

AS MENTIONED EARLIER, learning does not have to be a formal or structured process. We can incorporate continuous learning into our daily lives through small and simple actions. Here are some ways we can do this:

- Set aside time each week to read an article or book on a topic you are interested in.

- Watch educational videos or listen to podcasts during your commute or while doing chores.

• Take online quizzes, tests, or puzzles to develop skills such as critical thinking and problem-solving.

• Attend networking events and conferences related to your profession.

• Engage in discussions with colleagues or friends about various topics and gain knowledge through their insights and perspectives.

The Benefits of Continuous Learning for Our Overall Well-being

ENGAGING IN CONTINUOUS learning not only benefits our careers but also contributes to our overall well-being. By learning new skills and expanding our knowledge, we can improve our cognitive function, memory, and creativity. This can help us to be more efficient in our daily tasks and improve our problem-solving skills.

Continuous learning also keeps our minds active and engaged, reducing the risk of cognitive decline and dementia as we age. As we continue to learn and develop new skills, we are also challenging ourselves and stepping out of our comfort zones, which can boost our confidence and self-esteem.

Moreover, learning can be a stress-reliever and a form of self-care. Engaging in activities that we enjoy and that improve our skills can provide a sense of relaxation and fulfillment. It can also be a form of distraction from everyday stressors and help us recharge and refocus.

Conclusion

IN A WORLD THAT IS constantly evolving, it is essential to develop skills and engage in continuous learning to stay competitive and adaptable. This process not only benefits our careers but also contributes to our overall well-being by providing a sense of fulfillment, improving our cognitive function, and reducing stress. By incorporating continuous learning into our daily lives, we can continuously grow and nurture our whole selves.

In today's fast-paced world, the line between work and personal life can often feel blurred. Many people struggle with finding a balance between their careers and personal responsibilities, leading to increased stress and burnout. However, maintaining a healthy work-life balance is crucial for our overall well-being.

The Importance of Work-Life Balance Achieving work-life balance means finding a harmonious way to manage both our professional and personal lives. When we neglect one area, it can have a domino effect on the other, ultimately leading to burnout, decreased productivity, and a negative impact on our relation- ships and health. Finding a balance allows us to perform better in our careers, have more fulfilling personal lives, and maintain our physical and emotional well-being.

Managing Work-Related Stress Stress is an inevitable part of any career, but when it becomes chronic and overwhelming, it can affect our ability to function effectively. It's crucial to identify and manage work-related stress before it escalates and causes detrimental effects on our health.

• **Identify your stressors:** Take a few moments to reflect on what triggers stress in your work life. Is it a heavy workload, an unmanageable schedule, or a difficult coworker? Identifying these stressors is the first step in finding ways to reduce or eliminate them.

• **Set boundaries:** Often, we may feel pressured to constantly work and be available for our jobs. However, it's essential to set boundaries and have dedicated time for your personal life. This could mean turning off work notifications outside of work hours or saying no to tasks that will overwhelm you.

• **Prioritize self-care:** In the midst of a hectic work schedule, it's easy to neglect self-care. But taking care of ourselves is crucial for managing stress and maintaining a healthy work-life balance. Make time for activities that relax and rejuvenate you, such as exercise, meditation, or spending time with loved ones.

• **Don't be afraid to ask for help:** Many people struggle with asking for help, but it's essential to reach out when you're feeling overwhelmed or have too much on your plate. Whether it's delegating tasks at work or asking for support from family and friends, remember that it's okay to not do everything alone.

- **Practice stress-management techniques:** Find techniques that work for you to manage stress in the moment. These could include deep breathing, taking a short break, or practicing positive self-talk. Regularly incorporate these techniques throughout your workday to help reduce overall stress levels.

Balancing Personal Responsibilities Aside from our careers, we also have personal responsibilities to attend to, such as family, friends, household chores, and self-care. Balancing these responsibilities with work can be challenging, but it's essential to avoid burnout and maintain our overall well-being.

- **Create a schedule:** Having a structured schedule can help us better manage our time and balance our personal responsibilities with work. Set aside specific blocks of time for tasks such as spending time with family, running errands, or self-care activities.

- **Communicate with your loved ones:** Let your family and friends know your schedule and when you are available. This will help manage expectations and avoid feeling guilty when you need to prioritize work.

- **Delegate tasks:** Don't be afraid to delegate tasks to others, whether it's hiring a cleaning service or asking a friend to help with errands. Recognize that you don't have to do everything yourself, and it's okay to ask for help.

- **Take breaks and disconnect:** It's crucial to take breaks throughout the day to rest and recharge. Avoid checking work emails or messages during these breaks and disconnect from work entirely after work hours to give

yourself time to unwind and focus on your personal life.

• **Combine personal activities with work responsibilities:**
If possible, try to combine personal activities with your work
tasks. This could mean scheduling a doctor's appointment
during your lunch break or taking a walk with a friend
during a work call. This can help you maximize your time
and find balance in different areas of your life.

Finding a Support System Having a support system is crucial for
main- taining a healthy work-life balance. Whether it's a close friend,
family member, or a mentor, having someone to lean on during
challenging times can make a significant difference. A support system
can offer advice, help you see things from a different perspective, and
provide a listening ear when you need to vent.

• **Nurture supportive relationships:** Cultivate friendships
and relation- ships with individuals who support and
encourage you to find balance in your life. These individuals
can also hold you accountable and help you stick to your
boundaries and self-care routines.

• **Join a community or group:** Look for communities or
groups that share similar interests or goals. These can be a
great source of support and motivation, and you can learn
from others' experiences.

• **Seek guidance from a mentor:** A mentor can be a
valuable asset in helping you navigate your career and
personal life. They can offer guidance, share their
experiences, and offer a different perspective on challenges
you may face.

The Benefits of Work-Life Balance Aside from preventing burnout and improving overall well-being, there are many benefits to achieving work-life balance. These include:

- **Increased productivity:** When we take care of ourselves and our personal lives, we become more focused and productive in our careers.

- **Improved relationships:** Balancing work and personal life allows us to spend quality time with loved ones, strengthening relationships and creating happy memories.

- **Better overall health:** Chronic stress and neglecting self-care can have a significant impact on our physical and mental health. Balancing our responsibilities can help us maintain good health and prevent illness.

- **Greater sense of fulfillment:** When we have a healthy balance in our lives, we feel more satisfied and fulfilled. This can lead to a greater sense of purpose and happiness.

Final Thoughts Achieving work-life balance and managing stress is an ongoing process, and it's important to regularly reassess and make necessary adjustments. Remember, your well-being and overall happiness should always be a top priority. By finding balance in your career and personal life, you can cultivate a vibrant and fulfilling life.

Fitness and Well-being

P hysical fitness is often seen as something purely related to our outward appear- ance or the ability to perform physical tasks. However, it goes much deeper than that. The state of our physical well-being has a profound effect on all areas of our lives, including our relationships, career, and spirituality. In this section, we will explore the importance of physical fitness and how it can contribute to our overall well-being.

The Physical-Emotional Connection

OUR PHYSICAL AND EMOTIONAL states are deeply intertwined. When we neglect one, it can have a negative impact on the other. For example, if we are physically exhausted, it can lead to irritability or mood swings. On the other hand, if we are going through emotional turmoil, it can manifest as physical symptoms such as headaches or stomachaches.

Physical fitness helps to create a strong and balanced foundation for our emotional well-being. Regular exercise releases endorphins, also known as the "feel-good" hormones, which can help alleviate symptoms of anxiety and depression, and improve our overall mood. Additionally, physical activity helps to reduce stress and increase our ability to cope with difficult situations. It also provides a healthy outlet for any built-up tension or negative emotions.

The Mental Benefits of Physical Fitness

IN ADDITION TO THE positive effects on our emotions, physical fitness also has numerous benefits for our mental health. Regular exercise has been shown to improve cognitive function, memory, and concentration. When we exercise, our brain releases chemicals that help to improve our ability to focus and retain information. This can be especially beneficial for those with high-stress jobs or demanding careers.

Furthermore, physical activity has been linked to a reduced risk of developing mental health disorders such as depression and anxiety. It can also be used as a coping mechanism for those who already struggle with these conditions. By incorporating regular exercise into our daily routine, we are taking active steps towards maintaining our mental well-being.

Fueling Our Bodies for Optimal Performance

IN ORDER TO EFFECTIVELY engage in physical activity, our bodies require proper nutrition and hydration. Just like a car needs good quality fuel to operate at its best, our bodies need nutritious food to function optimally. Eating a well-balanced diet consisting of whole foods, lean protein, complex carbohydrates, and healthy fats can provide us with the energy and nutrients we need to perform at our best.

Proper nutrition is not just important for physical performance, but it also plays a crucial role in our overall health. A diet high in processed foods and unhealthy fats can increase the risk of chronic diseases such as heart disease, diabetes, and obesity. On the other hand, a nutritious diet can help prevent these diseases and promote a long and healthy life.

Designing an Effective Exercise Routine

WITH THE OVERWHELMING amount of information available on fitness and exercise, it can be challenging to know where to start. The key is to find a routine that works for you and your lifestyle. This can include a mix of different types of exercise, such as cardiovascular activities, strength training, and flexibility exercises.

It's also important to listen to your body and make modifications as needed. If you have any injuries or health conditions, it's essential to consult with a healthcare professional before starting any new fitness routine. They can provide guidance on exercises that are safe and beneficial for your specific needs.

The Importance of Rest and Recovery

WHILE IT'S IMPORTANT to engage in regular physical activity, it's equally important to rest and allow our bodies to recover. Overtraining can lead to burnout, injury, and other negative effects on our overall health. Incorporating rest days into our exercise routine is crucial for giving our bodies time to repair and recharge.

Additionally, proper rest and recovery also involve getting enough sleep each night. Lack of sleep not only affects our energy levels and mood but also has a significant impact on our physical health. It can lead to a weakened immune system, increased risk of chronic diseases, and higher levels of stress.

Mindful Movement and Stress Reduction

IN OUR FAST-PACED SOCIETY, it's common for us to mindlessly go through our exercise routines, focusing solely on achieving physical fitness goals. However, incorporating mindfulness into our movement can greatly enhance the benefits of physical activity. Paying attention to our bodies, breathing, and surroundings can help to reduce stress and increase our overall sense of well-being.

In addition to mindfulness, incorporating activities such as yoga or tai chi into our fitness routine can be highly beneficial for reducing stress and promoting relaxation. These practices not only improve our physical fitness but also help to cultivate a more peaceful and centered mind.

Finding Balance

PHYSICAL FITNESS IS vital for our overall well-being, but it's essential to find a balance that works for us. With the pressure to look a certain way or meet certain fitness goals, it's easy to become too focused on the physical aspects of fitness and neglect other areas of our lives. It's crucial to remember that our well-being is multidimensional, and neglecting one aspect can have a ripple effect on the others.

Finding balance also means listening to our bodies and respecting their limitations. Pushing too hard can result in injuries or burnout, ultimately hindering our progress. It's essential to find a balance between pushing ourselves and being gentle with our bodies when needed.

Incorporating Physical Fitness into Our Daily Lives

PHYSICAL ACTIVITY DOESN'T have to be a daunting task or a chore. There are countless ways to incorporate movement into our daily lives, such as taking the stairs instead of the elevator, going for a walk during our lunch break, or finding joy in activities such as dancing or gardening. The key is to find activities that we enjoy and that bring us closer to our physical fitness goals.

By making physical fitness a priority in our lives, we are not only taking care of our bodies but also nourishing our whole selves. It can have a positive impact on our relationships, career, and spirituality, and help us lead a more vibrant and fulfilling life. Remember, the journey to physical fitness is a lifelong process, and the most important thing is to find a routine that works for us and to listen to our bodies along the way.

Maintaining a regular exercise routine is crucial for our physical and mental well-being. However, with today's fast-paced lifestyle, it can be challenging to find the time and motivation to exercise consistently. That's why it's essential to design an effective exercise routine that fits your needs and lifestyle.

Why Exercise is Important for the Whole Self

REGULAR PHYSICAL ACTIVITY not only benefits our physical health but also plays a vital role in our emotional, mental, and spiritual well-being. Exercise releases endorphins, also known as the "feel-good" hormones, which can improve our mood and reduce stress levels. It also helps us maintain a healthy weight, improves cardiovascular health, and strengthens our muscles and bones.

Moreover, exercise is an excellent way to boost our confidence and self-esteem. When we set exercise goals and achieve them, we feel a sense of accomplishment, which can help improve our overall sense of self-worth. It also allows us to feel more in control of our bodies, which can positively impact our relationship with ourselves and our body image.

Finding the Right Type of Exercise for You

WHEN IT COMES TO EXERCISE, finding the right type for you is crucial. It's not just about choosing a workout that will give you the most significant physical benefits, but also one that you enjoy doing. If you don't enjoy the type of exercise you're doing, it's unlikely that you'll stick with it in the long run.

There are various types of exercises, including cardio, strength training, and flexibility exercises. It's essential to incorporate each type into your routine for a well-rounded workout. Some activities, such as yoga and Pilates, combine all three types of exercises, making them a great option for those looking for a diverse workout.

To find the right exercise for you, first, think about your fitness goals. Do you want to lose weight, build muscle, improve flexibility, or increase endurance? Once you have a clear goal, you can choose the type of exercise that can help you achieve it. For example, if your goal is to lose weight, you may want to focus on cardio exercises such as running or cycling.

It's also crucial to consider your physical limitations and any health conditions you may have. If you have a pre-existing injury, you may need to avoid high- impact exercises and focus on low-impact options. Always consult with a healthcare provider before starting a new exercise routine, especially if you have any underlying health concerns.

Creating an Effective Exercise Plan

ONCE YOU HAVE DECIDED on the type of exercise that is right for you, it's time to create a plan. Having a well-structured workout plan can help you stay motivated, track your progress, and ensure you don't overexert yourself.

When creating an exercise plan, consider the following factors:

- Frequency: How many days a week will you exercise?

- Duration: How long will each workout session be?

- Intensity: How challenging will your workouts be?

- Progression: How will you continually challenge your body and avoid plateauing?

The frequency and duration of your workouts will depend on your fitness level and personal goals. If you're just starting and are new to exercising, aim for at least three workout sessions per week, gradually increasing the frequency and duration as you build up your stamina.

Another essential factor to consider is intensity. It's vital to find a balance and not push your body beyond its limits. Start at a comfortable intensity level and gradually increase it over time. If you're unsure, a good rule of thumb is to exercise at a level where you can still hold a conversation.

To continue challenging your body and avoid plateauing, you can change up your exercises, increase the intensity, add weights, or try new forms of workouts.

Incorporating Fitness into Your Daily Life

IT CAN BE EASY TO MAKE excuses and not find the time to exercise. However, by incorporating fitness into our daily lives, it can become a natural and consistent habit. Here are some tips to help you incorporate fitness into your daily routine:

- Make workouts convenient: Choose a gym or workout facility that is close to your home or work, making it easier to fit into your schedule.

- Schedule your workouts: Treat your workout sessions as important ap- pointments that you cannot miss.

- Multitask: Combine exercise with other activities you enjoy, such as listening to audiobooks or podcasts while running or stretching.

- Take breaks at work: Sitting for extended periods can be harmful to our bodies. Take 5-10 minute breaks every hour to stretch or go for a walk.

- Choose active hobbies: Instead of spending your free time watching TV or scrolling through social media, engage in activities that require physical movement, such as hiking, dancing, or playing a sport.

- Use technology: There are countless fitness apps, trackers, and online workout classes available that you can use to stay motivated and organized.

It's essential to remember that fitness doesn't have to be a chore. Find ways to make it enjoyable and incorporate it into your daily life in a way that works for you.

Fueling Your Body for Optimal Performance

APART FROM REGULAR physical activity, proper nutrition is essential for maintaining a healthy body. Your diet can significantly impact your energy levels, endurance, and overall performance during exercise.

Aim to consume a well-balanced diet that includes lean proteins, complex carbohydrates, healthy fats, and plenty of fruits and vegetables. These foods provide the necessary nutrients and energy for your body to function at its best. It's also crucial to stay hydrated by drinking plenty of water throughout the day, especially before and after exercising.

Understanding the relationship between exercise and nutrition can also help you make smarter food choices. After a workout, your body needs to replenish energy and repair any damaged muscles. Consuming a post-workout snack or meal that includes protein, healthy fats, and carbohydrates can aid in muscle recovery and help you achieve your fitness goals.

Mindfulness and Exercise

IN TODAY'S FAST-PACED world, exercise is often perceived as just another item on our never-ending to-do lists. However, by incorporating mindfulness into our exercise routines, we can make it a more meaningful and beneficial experience for our whole self.

Mindful exercise involves being fully present and paying attention to our body and the sensations we experience during physical activity. It can help us connect with our bodies, reduce stress levels, and enhance the mind-body connection.

To incorporate mindfulness into your exercise routine, focus on your breath and body while exercising, and try to stay present instead of letting your mind wander. You can also try activities such as yoga or Tai chi, which emphasize mindfulness and can help you achieve a state of relaxation and focus.

Conclusion

DESIGNING AN EFFECTIVE exercise routine is essential for nourishing the whole self. It not only benefits us physically but also contributes to our emotional, mental, and spiritual well-being. By finding the right type of exercise, creating a well- structured plan, and making fitness a part of our daily lives, we can reap the numerous benefits that exercise has to offer. Remember to prioritize self-care and listen to your body, making adjustments as needed. With a consistent and mindful exercise routine, we can lead vibrant and healthy lives.

Eating is not just about satisfying physical hunger; it is also about nourishing our bodies and minds. The food we consume plays a crucial role in our overall well-being, affecting not just our physical health but also our emotional and mental states. In this section, we will dive deeper into the relationship between nutrition and our whole selves, and explore how we can cultivate healthy eating habits to support a vibrant life.

Understanding the Relationship Between Food and Health

YOU ARE WHAT YOU EAT, or so the saying goes. And while it may not be entirely true, there is some truth to it. The food we eat becomes the building blocks for our bodies, providing the necessary nutrients and energy for our bodily functions. But it's not just about the physical aspect; our diet also impacts our mood, energy levels, and overall well-being.

As a society, we are bombarded with different fad diets and conflicting information about what is considered "healthy" eating. However, the truth is that there is no one-size-fits-all approach when it comes to nourishing our bodies. Each person's dietary needs and preferences are unique, and it's essential to listen to our bodies and make choices that align with our individual needs.

Nutrients for Emotional Well-being

IT'S NO SECRET THAT our food choices can affect our emotions. We've all experienced the short-term effects of indulging in comfort foods when we're feeling down. However, what we eat can also impact our long-term emotional well-being.

Research has shown that certain nutrients can influence our mood and mental health. For example, omega-3 fatty acids found in fish, nuts, and seeds have been linked to lower rates of depression and anxiety. Antioxidant-rich foods, such as berries and dark leafy greens, can also help reduce inflammation in the body, which has been linked to mental health issues. Additionally, maintaining stable blood sugar levels through proper nutrition can help regulate our emotions and prevent mood swings.

Foods for Mental Clarity and Cognitive Function

JUST AS OUR BODIES need fuel to function correctly, our brains also require adequate nutrition to operate at their best. Certain nutrients, such as B vitamins, have been linked to increased brain function, memory, and focus. Healthy fats, such as those found in avocado and olive oil, are essential for brain health and have been shown to improve cognitive function. Eating a variety of whole, plant-based foods can provide the nutrients necessary for optimal brain function.

On the other hand, processed and sugary foods have been linked to decreased cognitive function and increased risk of cognitive decline later in life. High levels of sugar and unhealthy fats can hinder our brain's ability to think clearly and concentrate, leading to decreased productivity and motivation.

Fueling the Body for Physical Performance

IN ADDITION TO PROVIDING necessary nutrients for our bodies, the food we eat also directly impacts our physical performance. What we consume before, during, and after exercise has a significant influence on our energy levels, endurance, and recovery.

Before a workout, it's essential to fuel our bodies with complex carbohydrates for long-lasting energy. These can be found in whole grains, fruits, and vegetables. During exercise, it's crucial to stay hydrated and replenish electrolytes with water or sports drinks. After a workout, our bodies need protein to repair and build muscle tissue. Lean proteins, such as chicken, fish, and legumes, are excellent options for post-workout meals.

Filling our bodies with highly processed and sugary foods can not only hinder our physical performance but also lead to negative health consequences in the long run. It's crucial to listen to our bodies and fuel them with whole, nutrient-dense foods for optimal physical performance.

Implementing Healthy Eating Habits

NOW THAT WE UNDERSTAND the importance of nutrition for our whole selves, how can we actually implement healthy eating habits into our daily lives? Here are some tips to get started:

- Focus on whole, unprocessed foods: Strive to make the majority of your diet consist of whole grains, fruits, vegetables, and lean proteins.

- Meal prep and plan ahead: Taking the time to plan and prepare your meals ahead of time can help you stay on track and make healthier food choices.

• Listen to your body: Pay attention to how different foods make you feel and adjust your diet accordingly. This can help you determine your unique dietary needs and preferences.

• Stay hydrated: Drinking enough water is essential for overall health and can also help curb cravings for unhealthy foods.

• Practice mindful eating: Slow down and pay attention to the food you consume. This can help you connect with your body's hunger and fullness cues, preventing overeating.

• Allow for balance and flexibility: It's okay to enjoy occasional treats or indulge in your favorite foods in moderation. Remember that a healthy diet is about balance and not depriving yourself.

Conclusion

NUTRITION IS A VITAL aspect of taking care of our whole selves. By understanding the relationship between food and our health, we can make informed decisions about what we put in our bodies. Implementing healthy eating habits, along with nourishing our relationships, careers, fitness, and spirituality, can contribute to a balanced and vibrant life. Remember to listen to your body, stay hydrated, and practice mindful eating. Embrace the journey of nourishing the whole self and enjoy the benefits of a well-nourished and fulfilled life.

In today's fast-paced world, stress and overwhelm have become increasingly common. We often find ourselves constantly juggling multiple responsibilities and tasks, leading to burnout and negative effects on our overall well-being. This is where mindfulness can play a crucial role in managing stress and finding balance.

The Importance of Mindfulness

MINDFULNESS IS THE practice of being fully present in the moment, using our senses to focus on our surroundings and our thoughts. It is about being aware without judgment and coming back to the present whenever our minds start to wander. It allows us to let go of worries about the future or regrets about the past and instead focus on the present moment.

When we are mindful, we can better understand our emotions and reactions, and make conscious choices rather than being controlled by our automatic responses. This is especially important when it comes to managing stress. Instead of getting caught up in negative thoughts and emotions, we can acknowledge and observe them without attaching ourselves to them, allowing them to pass by without causing us harm.

Mindfulness Practices for Stress Reduction

THERE ARE MANY WAYS to incorporate mindfulness into our daily lives and reduce stress. Here are a few practices to try:

1. Meditation Meditation is a powerful tool for cultivating mindfulness and reducing stress. It involves sitting or lying down in a comfortable position and focusing on our breath while observing our thoughts without judgment. It can help clear our minds and calm our nervous systems, allowing us to be more present and focused in our daily lives.

Start by finding a quiet and comfortable place to sit or lie down for a few minutes. Close your eyes and take deep breaths, noticing the rise and fall of your chest. As thoughts come into your mind, simply observe them and bring your focus back to your breath. You may also try guided meditations or listen to calming music while meditating.

2. Mindful Movement Another way to practice mindfulness is through mindful movement, such as yoga, tai chi, or qigong. These practices involve slow and deliberate movements that focus on the breath, allowing us to release tension and stress from our bodies while increasing our mind-body connection. They also encourage us to be fully present and aware of our movements, thoughts, and sensations.

If you are new to mindful movement, consider taking a class or watching online videos to learn the proper techniques and postures. You can also incorporate these practices into your daily routine, such as taking a few minutes to stretch or do some yoga poses in the morning.

3. Gratitude Practice Expressing gratitude is a great way to shift our focus from stress and negativity to the present moment and all the good things in our lives. Practicing gratitude can help us appreciate the small things and find joy in the present, rather than constantly striving for the next big thing. It can also help us cultivate a more positive outlook and reduce stress.

Try keeping a gratitude journal and writing down a few things you are grateful for each day, whether it's a warm cup of tea, a hug from a loved one, or a beautiful sunset. You can also make it a habit to express gratitude out loud to someone each day, whether it's a friend, family member, or coworker.

4. Mindful Eating Eating mindfully can help us reconnect with our bodies and better understand our hunger and fullness cues. It also allows us to savor and enjoy our food fully, without distractions or rushing. This can be particularly helpful in reducing stress, as stress often leads to mindless or emotional eating.

To practice mindful eating, sit down at a table and remove any distractions, such as phones or TV. Take a few deep breaths before starting to eat and try to eat slowly, paying attention to the flavors, textures, and sensations of the food. Make an effort to chew slowly and fully and put down your utensils in between bites to fully experience your meal.

Benefits of Mindfulness for Stress Reduction

IN ADDITION TO REDUCING stress, mindfulness practices have many other benefits for our well-being. These include:

- Increased self-awareness and self-compassion

- Improved emotional regulation and resilience

- Better focus and concentration

- Positive effects on brain structure

- Reduced symptoms of anxiety, depression, and other mental health disor- ders

- Improved relationships and communication

- Overall sense of well-being and happiness

Making Mindfulness a Daily Practice

INCORPORATING MINDFULNESS into our daily lives takes time and effort, but the benefits are well worth it. Here are some tips for making mindfulness a regular practice:

- Start with short sessions: Instead of trying to meditate for an hour, start with just a few minutes each day and gradually increase the duration as you become more comfortable.

- Set reminders: It can be easy to forget to be mindful, especially when our lives are busy. Set reminders on your phone or leave sticky notes in visible places to bring your attention back to the present.

- Be patient and non-judgmental: Mindfulness is not something that can be mastered overnight, and there will be days when it may be more challenging to stay present. Be patient and kind to yourself, and don't judge yourself if you find your mind wandering during your practice.

- Experiment with different practices: Everyone's mindfulness practice may look different, so don't be afraid to try different techniques and find what works best for you.

With consistent practice, mindfulness can become a natural part of our daily routines, helping us better manage stress and nourish our whole selves.

In conclusion, mindfulness is an essential tool for reducing stress and finding balance in our lives. By practicing mindfulness, we can learn to be more present, aware, and in control of our thoughts and emotions, ultimately leading to a more vibrant and fulfilling life. Make time for mindfulness in your daily routine, and watch as it positively impacts all aspects of your well-being.

Cultivating Spirituality

5.1 Exploring Different Spiritual Practices

S pirituality is a deeply personal and individual experience that can bring a sense of purpose, connection, and inner peace to our lives. It is a journey of self-discovery and exploration, allowing us to tap into our inner wisdom and connect with something greater than ourselves. While spirituality can take many forms and mean different things to different people, it is ultimately about finding meaning and purpose in life.

In this section, we will explore different spiritual practices that can enhance our overall well-being and nourish our whole selves. These practices can help us cultivate a deeper sense of connection, find inner peace, and align our actions with our values and beliefs.

Meditation and Mindfulness

ONE OF THE MOST WIDELY recognized and practiced spiritual practices is meditation. Meditation involves training the mind to focus and redirect thoughts, allowing for increased awareness and a sense of calm. It can be done in various forms, such as mindfulness meditation, loving-kindness meditation, or transcendental meditation.

Mindfulness, on the other hand, is the practice of being fully present in the moment, without judgment. It involves paying attention to our thoughts, feelings, and sensations with curiosity and acceptance. Mindfulness can be incorporated into our daily lives through activities such as mindful eating, walking, or even washing dishes.

Both meditation and mindfulness have been shown to reduce stress, improve mental clarity, and enhance overall well-being. They can help us cultivate a greater sense of self-awareness, manage our emotions more effectively, and develop a deeper connection with ourselves and others.

Connecting with Nature and the Universe

ANOTHER POWERFUL SPIRITUAL practice is connecting with nature and the universe. Spending time in nature, whether it's hiking in the mountains, walking on the beach, or simply sitting in a park, can be a deeply spiritual experience. It allows us to reconnect with the natural world, appreciate its beauty, and feel a sense of awe and wonder.

When we connect with nature, we tap into something greater than ourselves. We realize that we are part of a vast and interconnected web of life. This sense of interconnectedness can bring a deep sense of peace, gratitude, and humility. It reminds us that we are not separate from the world around us but rather an integral part of it.

In addition to connecting with nature, exploring the universe can also be a spiritual practice. This can involve stargazing, learning about astronomy, or contemplating the mysteries of the cosmos. It can help us expand our perspective, appreciate the grandeur of the universe, and contemplate our place in it.

Rituals and Ceremonies

RITUALS AND CEREMONIES have been a part of human culture for thousands of years. They provide a structured and intentional way to connect with the sacred and mark significant moments in our lives. Rituals can take many forms, such as lighting candles, saying prayers, or performing specific actions with symbolic meaning.

Engaging in rituals and ceremonies can help us create a sense of meaning and purpose in our lives. They can provide a sense of continuity and connection with our ancestors and traditions. Whether it's celebrating a religious holiday, performing a personal ritual, or participating in a community ceremony, these practices can deepen our spiritual connection and nourish our souls.

Creative Expression

CREATIVE EXPRESSION is another powerful spiritual practice that allows us to tap into our inner selves and connect with something greater. Whether it's through art, music, dance, or writing, engaging in creative activities can be a deeply spiritual experience. It allows us to express our emotions, thoughts, and experiences in a unique and authentic way.

When we engage in creative expression, we enter a state of flow, where time seems to stand still, and we are fully immersed in the present moment. This state of flow can be deeply fulfilling and nourishing to our souls. It allows us to tap into our inner wisdom, connect with our intuition, and express our true selves.

Exploring different spiritual practices can be a transformative journey that enhances our overall well-being and nourishes our whole selves. Whether it's through meditation and mindfulness, connecting with nature and the universe, engaging in rituals and ceremonies, or expressing ourselves creatively, these practices can help us find meaning, purpose, and inner peace in our lives. By incorporating these practices into our daily routines, we can cultivate vibrant lives and nourish our whole selves.

The concept of spirituality often involves connecting with something greater than ourselves. For many people, this can manifest as a connection with nature and the universe. Whether we believe in a higher power or not, nature and the universe can offer a sense of peace, wonder, and perspective that can nourish our souls.

There is something inherently calming about being surrounded by nature. Studies have shown that spending time in nature can reduce stress, lower blood pressure, and improve overall well-being. It allows us to unplug from the constant demands of modern life and find solace in the simplicity and beauty of the natural world.

In addition to the physical benefits, connecting with nature can also have profound spiritual implications. Many spiritual traditions view the natural world as sacred and believe that it holds wisdom, healing, and connection. By spending time in nature, we can tap into this wisdom and connect with the universe in profound ways.

One way to connect with nature and the universe is through mindful appreciation. This involves intentionally focusing on the present moment and appreciating the beauty and wonder around us. It could be as simple as taking a walk in the park and noticing the sights, sounds, and smells of nature. Alternatively, it could involve stargazing and marveling at the vastness and complexity of the universe.

Another way to connect with nature and the universe is through rituals and traditions. Many spiritual practices involve rituals that honor nature and the cycles of the earth and the universe. These rituals can range from simple acts like lighting a candle or burning incense to more elaborate ceremonies involving dance and meditation. By engaging in these rituals, we can deepen our connection with the natural world and the greater universe.

The practice of grounding is also a powerful way to connect with nature and the universe. Grounding, also known as earthing, involves walking barefoot on the earth or touching the earth with our hands, allowing us to absorb the energies of the earth. This practice has been shown to bring a sense of calm and balance, and can also help us feel more connected to the earth and the universe.

A key aspect of connecting with nature and the universe is the idea of inter- connection. Everything in nature, from the tiniest bug to the largest tree, is connected in some way. By recognizing and honoring this interconnectedness, we can cultivate a sense of unity with all living beings and the universe as a whole. This can broaden our perspective and remind us that we are not alone in this world.

Similarly, the concept of impermanence, or the idea that all things are con- stantly changing, can be observed in nature and can help us cultivate a greater understanding of ourselves and the universe. By recognizing that everything is temporary and ever-evolving, we can let go of attachment and find peace in the present moment.

Through our connection with nature and the universe, we can also learn important lessons about life. For example, the changing of seasons can remind us of the natural cycles of life and the importance of letting go and embracing change. The resilience and adaptability of plants and animals can inspire us to overcome challenges and obstacles in our own lives.

Incorporating nature and the universe into our spiritual practices can also help us connect with our inner selves. By spending time in nature and observing the cycles and patterns of the natural world, we can gain a better understanding of our own inner rhythms and emotions. This can help us find balance and harmony within ourselves and with the world around us.

In conclusion, connecting with nature and the universe is a powerful way to nourish our spiritual selves. It allows us to tap into the wisdom and healing energy of the natural world and reminds us of our interconnectedness and impermanence. By incorporating this connection into our daily lives, we can deepen our spiritual practices and find a sense of peace and purpose in a fast-paced world. So take a moment to step outside, breathe in the fresh air, and connect with the beautiful world around you. You may be surprised by the profound impact it can have on your soul.

In our fast-paced world, it can be easy to get caught up in the chaos and lose sight of what truly matters. That is where meditation and mindfulness come in. These practices help us to slow down, center ourselves, and be present in the moment. They allow us to quiet the mind and cultivate inner peace.

The Benefits of Meditation and Mindfulness

MEDITATION AND MINDFULNESS have been practiced for thousands of years and have been proven to have numerous benefits for our mental, emotional, and spiritual well-being. Research has shown that regular meditation and mindfulness can reduce stress, anxiety, and depression, improve focus and concentration, and increase feelings of calm and contentment. These practices also have physical benefits such as lowering blood pressure, improving sleep, and boosting the immune system. As we nourish our minds and spirits through these practices, we also improve our overall health and well-being.

Getting Started with Meditation

MEDITATION IS SIMPLY the act of quieting the mind and focusing on the present moment. It can be done in many different ways, but here are some basic steps to get you started:

1. Find a quiet and comfortable place to sit. It can be a cushion or a chair, as long as you can sit with your back straight and both feet flat on the ground.

2. Set a timer for your desired meditation time. This can be anywhere from 5 minutes to an hour, depending on your preference and schedule.

3. Close your eyes and focus on your breath. Notice the inhale and exhale, and try to keep your mind from wandering.

4. When thoughts do arise, acknowledge them and then let them go, returning your focus to your breath.

5. When the timer goes off, take a moment to sit quietly and slowly open your eyes.

As you practice meditation, you may find it helpful to use guided meditations or visualization techniques. These can be found in books, online, or through apps. It is also important to remember that there is no right or wrong way to meditate. The key is to find a technique that works for you and to make it a consistent part of your daily routine.

Incorporating Mindfulness into Everyday Life

WHILE MEDITATION IS a specific practice, mindfulness can be incorporated into our daily lives in various ways. It is simply the act of being fully present in the moment, without judgment or distractions. Here are some suggestions for incorporating mindfulness into your everyday life:

1. Start your day with intention and purpose. Take a few moments in the morning to set an intention for the day and visualize how you want to feel and act.
2. Practice mindful eating. Pay attention to the flavors, textures, and smells of your food. Chew slowly and savor each bite.
3. Take breaks throughout the day to check in with yourself. Notice your thoughts and emotions without judgment, and take a few deep breaths to ground yourself.
4. Engage in a mindful activity, such as gardening, coloring, or listening to music. Focus on the activity and allow yourself to be fully present.
5. Practice gratitude by reflecting on what you are thankful for each day. This can help cultivate a sense of contentment and positivity in your life.

The key to mindfulness is to be fully present in each moment, without dwelling on the past or worrying about the future. It takes practice, but the more we incorporate mindfulness into our daily lives, the more it becomes a natural part of how we think and behave.

The Connection Between Mindfulness and Spirituality

MINDFULNESS IS INTEGRAL to many spiritual practices, as it allows us to connect with our inner selves and the world around us. By quieting the mind and being fully present, we can tap into our spiritual beliefs and values and cultivate a deeper understanding of ourselves and our place in the universe. Mindfulness can also help us to find more meaning and purpose in our lives and strengthen our relationship with a higher power if we believe in one.

Meditation and mindfulness can be powerful tools for spiritual growth and self- realization. As we cultivate a regular practice, we may find ourselves experiencing more moments of clarity and connection with our spiritual beliefs. This can help us to feel more at peace and in tune with ourselves and the world around us.

Combining Mindfulness with Other Aspects of the Whole Self

JUST AS WITH THE OTHER aspects of the whole self, mindfulness can greatly enhance our relationships, careers, and fitness goals. By incorporating mindfulness into our interactions with others, we can improve our communication and emotional intelligence, leading to stronger and more fulfilling relationships. In our careers, mindfulness can help us to stay focused and productive, leading to more meaningful and successful work. And in our fitness journey, being mindful can deepen our mind-body connection and help us to maintain healthy habits.

When combined with a healthy diet, mindfulness can also support our mental and emotional well-being by reducing stress, improving sleep, and boosting our mood. As we continue to nourish all aspects of the whole self, mindfulness can be another powerful tool in creating a balanced and vibrant life.

Conclusion

IN A WORLD THAT IS constantly moving and changing, it is more important than ever to take the time to slow down and nourish our minds and spirits. Meditation and mindfulness are practices that can greatly benefit our overall well-being and enhance the other aspects of the whole self. With regular practice, we can cultivate inner peace, strengthen our connection with our values and beliefs, and live more vibrant and fulfilling lives. Remember, the key is to find what works for you and make it a consistent part of your daily routine. By prioritizing these practices, we take a step towards nurturing the most important relationship we have - the one with ourselves.

Spirituality is often thought of as a search for a deeper connection with the universe, a higher power, or one's inner self. It can take many forms, such as organized religion, meditation, or connecting with nature. Whichever path you choose, cultivating spirituality can bring a sense of inner peace and purpose to your life.

Understanding the Importance of Spirituality

IN OUR MODERN SOCIETY, we often prioritize physical health and material success over our spiritual well-being. However, neglecting our spiritual needs can leave us feeling unfulfilled and disconnected. Research has shown that spirituality can contribute to improved mental health, decreased stress and anxiety, and increased overall life satisfaction.

Exploring Different Spiritual Practices

THERE IS NO ONE-SIZE-fits-all approach to spirituality. What works for one person may not work for another. It's important to explore different practices and find what resonates with you. This can include attending religious services, practicing mindfulness meditation, or engaging in self-reflection through journaling.

Connecting with Nature and the Universe

SPENDING TIME IN NATURE can be a spiritual experience for many people. It allows us to slow down, disconnect from technology, and connect with the world around us. Whether it's hiking in the mountains, swimming in the ocean, or even just sitting in a park, being in nature can bring a sense of peace and connectedness.

Meditation and Mindfulness

MEDITATION IS A POWERFUL tool for cultivating spirituality. It allows us to quiet the mind, focus on the present moment, and connect with our inner selves. Mindfulness, or being fully present in the moment, can also be practiced in our daily lives, such as paying attention to our breath while walking or eating.

Finding Inner Peace and Purpose

SPIRITUALITY CAN HELP us find inner peace and purpose by providing us with a sense of belonging and connection. It can give us a larger perspective on life and help us navigate through difficult times. It can also guide us in finding our personal values and purpose, leading us to live more fulfilling lives.

Creating a Spiritual Routine

INCORPORATING SPIRITUALITY into our daily lives can help us maintain a strong sense of inner peace and purpose. This can include setting aside specific times for meditation or prayer, attending religious services, or engaging in self-reflection practices. Creating a spiritual routine can also help us stay connected to our inner selves, even when life gets busy or chaotic.

The Role of Diet in Spiritual Practice

JUST AS OUR DIET CAN impact our physical and mental well-being, it can also play a role in our spiritual practice. Certain foods have been traditionally associated with enhancing spiritual experiences. For example, some religious practices have dietary restrictions, such as fasting or avoiding certain foods, to help practitioners connect with their spiritual beliefs.

Foods for Spiritual Well-being

INCORPORATING CERTAIN foods into our diet can also help us cultivate our spirituality. These foods often have calming and grounding effects, making them beneficial for practices that require focus and stillness. Examples include:

• Nuts and seeds: High in healthy fats and proteins, nuts and seeds help promote mental clarity and focus.

• Leafy greens: Packed with vitamins and minerals, greens can improve cognitive function and overall well-being.

- Berries: Rich in antioxidants, berries can help reduce stress and promote relaxation.

- Whole grains: Good sources of complex carbohydrates, whole grains can provide sustained energy and improve mood.

- Herbal teas: Herbal teas like chamomile or lavender have calming properties and can help reduce anxiety.

Mindful Eating

MINDFUL EATING, OR paying attention to the sensations of eating and being present in the moment, can also be a spiritual practice. By being fully present while eating, we can appreciate and be grateful for the nourishment food provides. It can also help us listen to our body's needs, rather than mindlessly consuming food.

Balancing Physical and Spiritual Nourishment

WHILE CERTAIN FOODS can support our spiritual practice, it's important to maintain a balanced approach to nourishing our bodies. This means listening to our body's signals of hunger and fullness, choosing a variety of nutritious foods, and practicing moderation and balance. By nourishing our physical bodies, we can support our overall well-being and have the energy and focus to continue our spiritual practices.

Final Thoughts

CULTIVATING SPIRITUALITY is a deeply personal and individualized journey. There is no right or wrong way to practice spirituality, and what works for one person may not work for another. The key is to remain open-minded, explore different practices, and find what brings a sense of inner peace and purpose to your life. By incorporating spirituality into our overall self-care and nourishment practices, we can create a more vibrant and fulfilling life.

The Power of Food

6.1 Understanding the Relationship Between Food and Health

F ood is not just a source of sustenance; it plays a crucial role in our overall health and well-being. The relationship between food and health is multifaceted, encompassing not only physical health but also emotional and mental well-being. In this section, we will explore the intricate connection between food and various aspects of our health, including emotional well-being, mental clarity, and physical performance.

Emotional Well-being and Food

THE FOOD WE CONSUME has a profound impact on our emotional well-being. Certain nutrients and compounds found in food can influence our mood, energy levels, and overall emotional state. For example, foods rich in omega-3 fatty acids, such as fatty fish, walnuts, and flaxseeds, have been linked to a reduced risk of depression and improved overall mental health. These fatty acids play a crucial role in brain function and help regulate neurotransmitters associated with mood.

Additionally, foods rich in antioxidants, such as berries, dark chocolate, and leafy greens, can help reduce oxidative stress in the body. Oxidative stress has been linked to increased risk of depression and anxiety. By incorporating these antioxidant-rich foods into our diet, we can support our emotional well-being and promote a positive mood.

Furthermore, the gut-brain connection highlights the importance of a healthy digestive system in maintaining emotional balance. The gut microbiome, a collection of microorganisms in our digestive tract, plays a significant role in producing neurotransmitters and regulating mood. Consuming a diet rich in fiber, prebiotics, and probiotics can support a healthy gut microbiome and positively impact our emotional well-being.

Mental Clarity and Cognitive Function

JUST AS FOOD AFFECTS our emotions, it also has a profound impact on our mental clarity and cognitive function. The brain requires a steady supply of nutrients to function optimally, and certain foods can enhance cognitive performance.

Omega-3 fatty acids, once again, play a crucial role in supporting brain health. Research suggests that these fatty acids can improve memory, attention, and overall cognitive function. Including sources of omega-3 fatty acids, such as fatty fish, chia seeds, and walnuts, in our diet can help nourish our brain and enhance mental clarity.

Moreover, foods rich in antioxidants, such as blueberries, spinach, and green tea, have been shown to protect the brain from oxidative stress and reduce the risk of cognitive decline. These antioxidants help combat inflammation and promote healthy brain function.

In addition to specific nutrients, maintaining stable blood sugar levels is essential for optimal cognitive function. Consuming a balanced diet that includes complex carbohydrates, lean proteins, and healthy fats can help regulate blood sugar levels and provide a steady supply of energy to the brain.

Physical Performance and Food

FOOD IS THE FUEL THAT powers our bodies, and the right choices can significantly impact our physical performance. Whether engaging in regular exercise or simply going about our daily activities, the foods we consume can enhance our energy levels, endurance, and overall physical well-being.

Carbohydrates are the primary source of energy for our bodies, and consuming the right types and amounts of carbohydrates is crucial for optimal physical per- formance. Complex carbohydrates, such as whole grains, fruits, and vegetables, provide a slow and steady release of energy, sustaining us throughout the day. On the other hand, simple carbohydrates, found in sugary snacks and processed foods, can lead to energy crashes and hinder physical performance.

Protein is another essential nutrient for physical performance. It plays a vital role in muscle repair and growth, making it crucial for individuals engaging in regular exercise or strength training. Including lean sources of protein, such as chicken, fish, tofu, and legumes, in our diet can support muscle recovery and enhance physical performance.

Furthermore, proper hydration is essential for optimal physical performance. Staying hydrated helps regulate body temperature, lubricate joints, and trans- port nutrients to cells. Water is the best choice for hydration, but consuming electrolyte-rich beverages, such as coconut water or sports drinks, can be benefi- cial during intense physical activity.

In conclusion, the relationship between food and health is intricate and mul- tifaceted. The foods we consume have a significant impact on our emotional well-being, mental clarity, and physical performance. By understanding this relationship and making conscious choices about the foods we eat, we can nourish our whole selves and cultivate vibrant lives.

Emotions are a crucial component of our overall well-being. They can greatly influence how we feel, think, and behave. When we experience positive emotions such as joy, love, and contentment, we are more likely to feel fulfilled and happy. Conversely, negative emotions like sadness, anger, and fear can impact our mental, emotional, and physical state in detrimental ways. The food we eat can play a significant role in regulating and supporting our emotional state.

Certain nutrients have been found to have a direct impact on our emotional well-being. These include vitamins, minerals, amino acids, and fatty acids. Our body requires a balance of these nutrients to function optimally, and when we are deficient in any of them, it can affect our mood and emotions.

Vitamin B-12, also known as cobalamin, is essential for maintaining a healthy nervous system. It is involved in the production of serotonin and dopamine, two neurotransmitters that regulate mood, happiness, and feelings of well-being. Low levels of B-12 have been linked to depression and cognitive decline. It is found in animal products such as meat, eggs, and dairy, but can also be taken as a supplement for those who follow a plant-based diet.

Omega-3 fatty acids are known for their anti-inflammatory properties, but they also play a crucial role in emotional well-being. Studies have found that individuals with higher levels of omega-3s in their diet have lower rates of depression and anxiety. These healthy fats are found primarily in fatty fish such as salmon, sardines, and mackerel, as well as in certain plant-based sources such as flaxseeds, chia seeds, and walnuts.

Magnesium is a mineral that is often overlooked, but it is essential for our overall health, including emotional well-being. This mineral helps relieve stress, promote relaxation, and improve sleep quality. It also plays a role in the production of serotonin, the neurotransmitter responsible for happiness and well-being. Good sources of magnesium include leafy green vegetables, whole grains, nuts, and seeds.

Another mineral that is crucial for emotional well-being is zinc. It is involved in the production and function of neurotransmitters such as serotonin and dopamine, as well as regulating the body's response to stress. Zinc deficiency has been linked to depression, anxiety, and mood disorders. Foods rich in zinc include oysters, beef, chicken, dairy, and legumes.

Amino acids are the building blocks of protein and play a vital role in the body's functions and processes. Some amino acids are particularly beneficial for managing stress and improving emotional well-being. These include tryptophan, which is converted into serotonin, and tyrosine, which is converted into dopamine. Good sources of these amino acids include turkey, chicken, fish, dairy, beans, nuts, and seeds.

In addition to specific nutrients, the quality and variety of food we consume can also impact our emotional well-being. For example, research has shown that consuming a diet rich in fruits, vegetables, and whole grains is associated with a lower risk of depression and anxiety. On the other hand, a diet high in processed foods, sugar, and unhealthy fats has been linked to an increased risk of these mental health disorders.

Furthermore, the act of preparing and sharing meals with loved ones can also have a positive impact on our emotional well-being. It fosters a sense of connection and promotes the release of oxytocin, a hormone that promotes feelings of trust and bonding. Eating together also allows for social support and can help reduce stress and promote relaxation.

When it comes to emotional well-being, it is also essential to maintain stable blood sugar levels. Low blood sugar has been linked to irritability, mood swings, and fatigue, while high blood sugar can lead to anxiety and oxidative stress. Therefore, it is crucial to consume a balanced diet that includes complex carbohydrates, healthy fats, and lean protein to keep blood sugar levels stable and promote emotional stability.

In addition to food, hydration is also crucial for our emotional well-being. Dehydration can cause irritability, confusion, and fatigue, while staying hydrated can improve energy levels, cognitive function, and mood. Aim to drink at least eight glasses of water per day and increase your intake if you are physically active or in hot weather.

One final aspect to consider when talking about nutrients for emotional well- being is the gut-brain connection. Our gut health plays a significant role in regulating mood and emotions. A diverse, balanced microbiome can produce neurotransmitters, such as serotonin and dopamine, that can influence our emotional state. On the other hand, an imbalanced gut microbiome has been linked to anxiety, depression, and other mental health disorders.

To support a healthy gut, it is important to consume a diet rich in prebiotic and probiotic foods. Prebiotics are indigestible fibers that act as fuel for the beneficial bacteria in our gut, while probiotics are live bacteria that can help restore balance to our microbiome. Good sources of prebiotics include garlic, onions, bananas, and artichokes, while probiotics can be found in fermented foods such as yogurt, kefir, and sauerkraut.

In conclusion, our emotional well-being is affected by a variety of factors, including the food we eat. By consuming a diet rich in essential nutrients, such as vitamins, minerals, amino acids, and fatty acids, we can support and regulate our moods and emotions. It is also crucial to maintain a balanced and diverse diet, stay hydrated, and foster a healthy gut microbiome to promote emotional well-being. Remember, food is not just fuel for our bodies, but also for our minds and souls.

In our fast-paced society, we often prioritize productivity and efficiency over our own well-being. This can lead to neglecting our mental and cognitive health, which are essential for our overall functioning and success in life. Thankfully, there are certain foods that can help improve our mental clarity and cognitive function. Let's explore some of these foods and how they can benefit our brains.

The Power of Antioxidants

ANTIOXIDANTS ARE COMPOUNDS found in various foods that protect our cells from damage by free radicals. These damaging molecules can contribute to cognitive decline and diseases like Alzheimer's and Parkinson's. Therefore, consuming foods high in antioxidants can help preserve our brain health. Some common sources of antioxidants include berries, dark chocolate, and green tea.

Omega-3 Fatty Acids

OMEGA-3 FATTY ACIDS are essential for brain function and development. They are found in high levels in fatty fish such as salmon, tuna, and sardines. These healthy fats can help improve memory, focus, and even mood. For those who do not consume fish, plant-based sources of omega-3s include chia seeds, flaxseeds, and walnuts.

Nourishing Nuts and Seeds

NUTS AND SEEDS ARE packed with essential vitamins and minerals that support brain health. They are rich in magnesium, which can help improve memory and learning, and zinc, which aids in overall cognitive functioning. Almonds, cashews, pumpkin seeds, and sunflower seeds are just a few examples of brain-boosting nuts and seeds.

Dark Leafy Greens

DARK LEAFY GREENS LIKE spinach, kale, and collard greens are rich in nutrients that can benefit our mental clarity and cognitive function. They are high in vitamins A, C, and K, which support brain cell growth and communication. Additionally, they contain folate, which can help protect against age-related cognitive decline.

Whole Grains

OUR BRAINS NEED A STEADY supply of glucose to function properly, and whole grains can provide this sustained energy. Whole grains like brown rice, quinoa, and oatmeal are high in complex carbohydrates, which take longer to break down and provide a slow release of glucose to the brain. This can help improve memory and concentration.

The Role of Gut Health

THERE IS A STRONG LINK between our gut and brain health, known as the gut-brain connection. The bacteria in our gut produce neurotransmitters that can impact our mood, cognition, and behavior. Therefore, it is important to consume foods that promote a healthy gut microbiome, such as probiotics found in yogurt, kefir, and fermented foods like sauerkraut.

The Benefits of Berries

BERRIES ARE NOT ONLY a delicious snack, but they also offer numerous brain- boosting benefits. Blueberries, in particular, have been shown to improve cognitive function and memory. This is due to their high levels of anthocyanins, a type of antioxidant that can help protect our brains from oxidative stress. Other types of berries like strawberries, raspberries, and blackberries also offer similar benefits.

The Magic of Caffeine

FOR MANY OF US, OUR morning coffee is a daily ritual. But did you know that caffeine can also benefit our mental clarity and cognitive function? This natural stimulant can help improve focus, alertness, and even memory. However, it is important to consume caffeine in moderation and not rely on it too heavily to avoid negative side effects.

Dark Chocolate, the Brain Food

DARK CHOCOLATE, SPECIFICALLY those with at least 70% cacao, contains high levels of flavonoids, which can help improve brain function. These compounds can increase blood flow to the brain, leading to improved cognitive performance. Additionally, dark chocolate has also been linked to improved mood and reduced stress levels, making it a delicious and beneficial treat for our brains.

The Importance of Staying Hydrated

THOUGH NOT TECHNICALLY a food, staying hydrated is crucial for our brain health. Our brains are made up of mostly water, and dehydration can lead to fatigue, difficulty concentrating, and impaired cognitive function. Drinking enough water throughout the day can help maintain optimal brain function and improve productivity.

Conclusion

INCORPORATING THESE brain-boosting foods into our diets can help us maintain mental clarity, improve our cognitive function, and prevent age-related decline. Additionally, eating a balanced diet rich in nutrients can also improve our overall well-being and contribute to a healthier and more nourished whole self. Remember, food is not only fuel for our bodies but also for our brains. Choose wisely, and savor the benefits of a well-nourished mind.

When we think of fueling our bodies, we often think of food as simply providing us with energy or sustenance to survive. However, what we eat can also have a significant impact on our physical performance. Just like a car needs high-quality fuel to run efficiently, our bodies require proper nutrition to function at their best. In this section, we will discuss the role of diet in physical performance and explore the types of foods that can help us reach our fitness goals.

The Connection Between Diet and Physical Performance

OUR BODIES ARE COMPLEX machines that require a balance of nutrients to perform at their peak. When it comes to physical performance, diet plays a crucial role in providing us with the energy, strength, and endurance we need to excel in our fitness routines. Whether you are an athlete training for a competition or simply someone looking to improve their overall physical health, paying attention to your diet is essential.

Without the right fuel, our bodies can struggle to keep up during physical activities, leading to fatigue, muscle cramps, and even injuries. On the other hand, when we provide our bodies with the proper nutrients, we can enhance our physical performance and achieve our fitness goals more efficiently.

Key Nutrients for Physical Performance

TO FUEL OUR BODIES for physical performance, we need to ensure we are consuming an adequate amount of key nutrients. These include:

Carbohydrates Carbohydrates are the primary source of energy for our bodies. They are broken down into glucose and provide us with the fuel we need for physical activity. Complex carbohydrates, such as whole grains, vegetables, and fruits, provide a slow and steady release of energy, making them ideal for activities that require endurance.

Protein Protein is crucial for building and repairing muscle tissue, making it essential for maintaining and improving physical strength. It also plays a role in energy production and can help improve athletic performance. It is recommended to consume protein both before and after exercise to support muscle recovery.

Healthy Fats Contrary to popular belief, fats are an essential part of a well- rounded diet, and they can also contribute to our physical performance. Healthy fats, such as those found in avocados, nuts, and fish, provide long-lasting energy and help reduce inflammation in the body, making them beneficial for recovery after intense physical activity.

Hydration Last but certainly not least, staying hydrated is crucial for physical performance. Water plays a vital role in regulating body temperature, aiding in digestion, and transporting nutrients to our muscles. It is essential to drink water before, during, and after exercise to replenish any fluids lost through sweat.

Foods to Support Physical Performance

NOW THAT WE UNDERSTAND the key nutrients for physical performance, let's explore the types of foods that can provide us with these nutrients:

Whole Grains Whole grains, such as quinoa, brown rice, and whole-grain bread, are a great source of complex carbohydrates. They provide a slow release of energy, making them ideal for sustaining endurance during physical activities.

Lean Proteins Protein is essential for building and maintaining muscle mass, making it a crucial nutrient for physical performance. Lean protein sources, such as chicken, fish, and tofu, are low in saturated fat and provide necessary amino acids for muscle repair.

Healthy Fats As mentioned earlier, healthy fats are an essential part of a well-rounded diet for physical performance. Avocados, nuts, and fatty fish like salmon are excellent sources of healthy fats that provide lasting energy and support muscle recovery.

Fruits and Vegetables Fruits and vegetables are filled with essential vitamins, minerals, and antioxidants that can support physical performance. Dark leafy greens like spinach and kale are rich in iron, which helps carry oxygen to our muscles, while fruits like bananas and berries provide quick and convenient sources of carbohydrates and energy.

Water and Electrolyte-Rich Beverages Staying hydrated is crucial for physical performance, especially during intense physical activity. Along with drinking plain water, electrolyte-rich beverages like coconut water and sports drinks can help replenish lost fluids and electrolytes during prolonged exercise.

Creating a Balanced Diet for Physical Performance

JUST LIKE WITH ANY aspect of our whole selves, balance is key when it comes to fueling our bodies for physical performance. A well-rounded diet that includes all the essential nutrients can help us achieve our fitness goals and improve our overall physical health.

To create a balanced diet for physical performance, it is important to:

- Eat a variety of foods from all food groups to ensure we are consuming all necessary nutrients.

- Pay attention to portion sizes to avoid consuming more calories than we need.

- Avoid highly processed and sugary foods that can cause energy crashes and inflammation in the body.

- Stay hydrated by drinking water throughout the day and increasing intake during physical activity.

Adopting a balanced diet can take time and effort, but the benefits for our physical performance can be significant. By fueling our bodies with the right nutrients, we can enhance our physical performance, avoid injuries, and improve our overall well-being.

Incorporating the foods discussed in this section into our diets can also have positive effects on our mental and emotional well-being. Proper nutrition can help boost energy levels, improve mood, and reduce stress, allowing us to perform at our best in all areas of our lives.

Conclusion

DIET PLAYS A CRITICAL role in our physical performance, providing us with the energy and nutrients needed to excel in our fitness routines. Consuming a balanced diet that includes the key nutrients discussed in this section can help us reach our fitness goals and improve our overall physical health.

Remember, our bodies are unique, and it may take some trial and error to find the right balance of nutrients that work best for us. By paying attention to what we eat and making conscious choices about our diets, we can nourish the whole self and achieve vibrant lives. So choose to fuel your body with the best, and watch as your physical performance improves along with your overall well-being.

Creating a Balanced Lifestyle

I n earlier chapters, we explored the importance of having healthy relationships, a fulfilling career, a regular fitness routine, and a deep connection with spirituality in maintaining a nourished and vibrant life. However, looking at each of these aspects separately is not enough. To truly nourish ourselves and thrive, we need to find ways to integrate all of these elements into our daily lives.

Our relationships, career, fitness, and spirituality are all intertwined and impact each other in various ways. Ignoring one aspect can have a ripple effect and create imbalances in other areas of our lives. For example, constant stress from work can negatively affect our relationships and overall well-being, or neglecting spiritual practices can lead to feelings of emptiness and lack of purpose in our career.

Integrating these four aspects involves finding a balance and creating a cohesive lifestyle that prioritizes each element. It requires conscious effort and a willingness to make changes and adjustments as needed. Here are some ways to integrate relationships, careers, fitness, and spirituality for a more nourished and vibrant life:

Finding a Balance

TO INTEGRATE RELATIONSHIPS, careers, fitness, and spirituality, we need to find balance among them. This means not only dedicating time and energy to each aspect but also recognizing when one element may be taking too much focus or causing an imbalance. For example, if you find yourself constantly working and neglecting your relationships, it may be time to reevaluate your priorities and make adjustments accordingly.

To find balance, it's important to understand your needs and what makes you feel nourished in each area. This also means understanding the needs of those around you and how you can support each other in leading a balanced life. It may require setting boundaries and being intentional with your time and energy.

Developing Healthy Habits and Routines

INTEGRATING RELATIONSHIPS, careers, fitness, and spirituality also involves estab- lishing healthy habits and routines that support all four aspects. This may include making time to connect with loved ones, setting goals and priorities in your career, prioritizing exercise and physical activity, and incorporating daily spiritual practices into your routine.

It may also involve letting go of harmful habits or behaviors that may be hindering your progress and creating imbalances. This could be something as simple as reducing screen time and spending more quality time with loved ones, or as significant as quitting a job that is causing stress and exploring new career opportunities.

Finding Balance in a Fast-Paced World

IN TODAY'S FAST-PACED and constantly connected world, finding balance can be challenging. With the constant demands and distractions, it's easy to get caught up in one aspect of our lives and neglect the others.

To overcome this challenge, it's essential to prioritize and make intentional choices. This may mean saying no to certain opportunities or commitments that do not align with your values and priorities. It may also involve setting boundaries and creating designated times to focus on each aspect of your life.

Self-Care and Self-Reflection

INTEGRATING RELATIONSHIPS, careers, fitness, and spirituality also involves taking care of ourselves and making time for self-reflection. Self-care is not a luxury; it's a necessity for our overall well-being. It involves setting aside time for activities that recharge and nourish us, such as exercise, meditation, reading, or spending time in nature.

Self-reflection allows us to check-in with ourselves and gain clarity and perspective on our lives. It can also help us identify imbalances and areas that require more attention and focus. Regular self-reflection can lead to growth and personal development, improving all areas of our lives.

Integrating relationships, careers, fitness, and spirituality is an ongoing and ever-evolving process. It requires a conscious effort to prioritize and balance each element in our lives. By finding a balance, developing healthy habits, and making time for self-care, we can create a cohesive and nourishing lifestyle that supports our overall well-being and helps us thrive. Remember, it's not about perfection, but about progress and continually striving towards a more vibrant and fulfilling life.

The foundation of living a vibrant life is built upon the habits and routines we develop. Our habits and routines are the daily actions that shape our lives, and ultimately determine our overall well-being.

When it comes to nourishing the whole self, it is crucial to establish healthy habits and routines in all four aspects of our lives – relationships, careers, fitness, and spirituality. These daily actions not only help us maintain a balanced and fulfilling life, but also contribute to our overall health and vitality.

In this section, we will explore how to develop healthy habits and routines in each aspect of our lives, and how they can support our well-being.

Cultivating Healthy Relationship Habits

HEALTHY RELATIONSHIPS are essential for our emotional and mental well-being. They provide a sense of belonging, support, and love that can help us navigate through life's challenges. But like anything worth having, healthy relationships require effort and cultivation.

One vital habit to develop in our relationships is effective communication. This involves actively listening to others, expressing ourselves clearly, and practicing empathy and emotional intelligence. Effective communication lays the foundation for healthy connections and fosters understanding and respect among individuals.

In addition to communication, setting boundaries is another crucial habit for maintaining healthy relationships. Boundaries help us respect our own needs and the needs of others, and prevent us from becoming overwhelmed or taken advantage of. We must also be willing to work through conflicts and resolve them in a healthy manner. This involves being open and honest, actively listening, and finding solutions that work for everyone involved.

Ultimately, cultivating supportive relationships involves prioritizing the people who bring positivity and support into our lives, and distancing ourselves from those who drain our energy and well-being. It's important to regularly evaluate our relationships and make adjustments as needed to ensure they align with our values and goals.

Nurturing Healthy Career Habits

OUR CAREERS PLAY A significant role in our lives, as they often define our purpose and provide financial stability. However, it's easy to fall into unfulfilling work habits and routines that can lead to burnout and dissatisfaction.

To nurture our careers and find true fulfillment, we must first define our values, passions, and goals. This will help guide us towards a career that aligns with our whole self and provides a sense of purpose and meaning. Once we have a clear direction, setting realistic goals and effectively managing our time is crucial for staying on track and achieving success.

Continuously developing new skills and learning is also essential for keeping our careers enriching and avoiding stagnation. This can involve taking courses, attending workshops, or seeking out new experiences and challenges.

Maintaining work-life balance is another important habit for our careers. This means finding a balance between our work and personal lives, and prioritizing self-care and mental well-being. Practicing stress management techniques such as mindfulness and taking breaks when needed can also contribute to a healthier work life.

Integrating Healthy Fitness Habits

PHYSICAL FITNESS IS crucial for maintaining a healthy body and mind. However, many of us struggle to develop and maintain healthy exercise habits. The key is finding activities that we enjoy and making them a regular part of our routines.

It's essential to start with realistic goals and gradually increase the intensity and duration of our workouts. Starting with small achievable goals can prevent burnout and help us stay motivated to continue.

In addition to regular exercise, developing healthy eating habits is also crucial for maintaining fitness. Fueling our bodies with nutrient-rich foods can support our physical performance and help us feel energized and clear-headed.

Lastly, incorporating mindfulness and stress reduction practices into our fitness routines can help us listen to our body's needs and avoid overexertion or injury.

Cultivating Healthy Spiritual Habits

SPIRITUAL PRACTICES can provide a sense of purpose, fulfillment, and inner peace. Just like any other aspect of our lives, developing healthy spiritual habits can help us cultivate a deeper connection with ourselves and the world around us.

Exploring different spiritual practices and finding ones that resonate with us is the first step towards spiritual nourishment. This can include meditation, prayer, yoga, nature walks, and other activities that bring a sense of peace and connection.

Consistency is key when it comes to developing healthy spiritual habits. Making time for these practices daily or weekly can help us stay grounded and maintain a sense of balance even during life's inevitable challenges.

Finding Balance in a Fast-Paced World

IN TODAY'S FAST-PACED world, it can be challenging to find a balance between all four aspects of our lives. It's vital to remember that balance is not about equally dividing our time and energy among these aspects, but rather about prioritizing what is most important to us and making time and space for each aspect in our lives.

One way to create balance is by setting boundaries and learning to say no to activities and commitments that do not align with our values and goals. It's also essential to regularly check in with ourselves and make sure we are not neglecting any aspect of our lives.

Practicing self-care and self-reflection is also crucial for finding balance. Taking time for ourselves to rest and recharge can help us maintain a healthy mind, body, and spirit. Reflecting on our choices and habits can also help us identify areas where we may need to make adjustments to create a better balance.

Incorporating Habits and Routines in our Lives

DEVELOPING HEALTHY habits and routines in all four aspects of our lives is crucial for nourishing our whole selves. These habits and routines may look different for each individual, but the key is finding what works best for us and incorporating them consistently into our lives.

It's important to remember that building habits takes time and patience. It may not be easy to break old patterns and develop new ones, but the effort is well worth it in the long run. Gradually implementing small changes and being consistent in our actions can lead to significant improvements in our physical, mental, and emotional well-being.

Incorporating these habits and routines into our lives may also require some trial and error. What works for one person may not work for another, and that's okay. It's essential to be open to trying new things and adjusting as we go along to find what works best for us.

In conclusion, developing healthy habits and routines in all aspects of our lives is crucial for nourishing the whole self and living a vibrant and fulfilling life. By prioritizing effective communication and boundaries in relationships, finding fulfillment and balance in our careers, incorporating regular exercise and healthy eating habits, and nurturing our spiritual well-being, we can create a life that supports our overall well-being. It may take time and effort, but the result is a truly vibrant and thriving life.

In our modern society, everything moves at a rapid pace. We are constantly bombarded with information and expectations, making it easy to feel over- whelmed and out of balance. This is especially true when it comes to managing relationships, careers, fitness, and spirituality.

As we strive to excel in each of these areas, it can be easy to neglect one or more aspects of our lives. We may become too consumed with work, neglecting our relationships and our physical health. Or, we may focus too heavily on our spirituality and neglect our career goals.

The key to finding balance in a fast-paced world is to prioritize and manage our time effectively. This means setting realistic goals and boundaries for ourselves. It also means being mindful of our energy levels and making time for self-care and self-reflection.

Prioritizing and Managing Time

ONE OF THE FIRST STEPS towards finding balance is to prioritize our tasks and manage our time effectively. This requires being honest with ourselves about what is truly important to us and what can be put on the backburner. We often feel pressure to do it all, but the reality is that we only have so much time and energy.

Start by making a list of your top priorities in each area of your life – relationships, career, fitness, and spirituality. This will help you identify where you may be neglecting one aspect in favor of another. Then, make a schedule for yourself and block out dedicated time for each priority. This could mean setting aside an evening each week for a date with your partner, or carving out an hour each day for exercise and self-care.

It's also important to set boundaries for yourself and stick to them. This means learning to say "no" to things that are not aligned with your priorities. It can be difficult to turn down opportunities or commitments, but it's crucial for maintaining balance and avoiding burnout.

Mindfulness and Self-Care

IN A FAST-PACED WORLD, we often feel like we have to keep moving and doing in order to be productive and successful. However, taking time for stillness and self-care is just as important for our overall well-being. Being mindful of our energy levels and our need for rest and rejuvenation is crucial for finding balance.

We can practice mindfulness in various ways, such as meditation, yoga, or simply taking a few minutes each day to slow down and focus on our breath. This helps us tune in to our body and mind, allowing us to recognize when we need a break or some self-care.

Self-care can include anything that brings us joy and helps us recharge – whether that's taking a bath, reading a book, or spending time in nature. It's important to make time for these activities, even if it means saying no to other commitments or making adjustments to our schedule.

Simplifying and Letting Go

ANOTHER IMPORTANT ASPECT of finding balance in a fast-paced world is learning to simplify and let go. We often feel the need to accumulate possessions, achievements, and even relationships in order to feel successful and happy. However, this can actually lead to feelings of overwhelm and imbalance.

Take some time to evaluate your life and identify areas where you may be holding on to too much. This could be physical possessions that you no longer need, commitments or responsibilities that you can delegate or let go of, or even toxic relationships that are draining your energy.

Learning to let go of what no longer serves us can be a powerful tool for finding balance and creating space for what truly matters in our lives.

Disconnecting to Reconnect

IN A WORLD WHERE WE are constantly connected through technology and social media, it can be difficult to disconnect and be present in the moment. However, taking breaks from technology and disconnecting from the constant stream of information can greatly contribute to our overall well-being.

Make it a priority to disconnect and be fully present in your relationships, your work, and your self-care activities. This means putting away your phone and focusing on the present moment and the people around you. It also means taking breaks from technology and allowing your mind to rest and recharge.

Doing these things regularly can help us feel more connected to ourselves, our loved ones, and the world around us. It also allows us to recharge and approach the fast-paced world with a fresh perspective and renewed energy.

Embracing Imperfection

IN A WORLD THAT VALUES productivity, success, and perfection, it can be difficult to embrace our imperfections and surrender control. However, striving for perfection can often lead to feelings of inadequacy and burnout.

Instead, let go of the pressure to be perfect and embrace imperfection as a natural part of life. This includes accepting that sometimes things will not go as planned and that it's okay to make mistakes.

Remember, balance is not about achieving perfection in all areas of life, but rather finding a sense of harmony and contentment amidst the chaos.

Conclusion

FINDING BALANCE IN a fast-paced world is an ongoing journey, and it requires making intentional choices and adjustments in our daily lives. By prioritizing, setting boundaries, practicing self-care, simplifying, disconnecting, and embracing imperfection, we can create a more balanced and fulfilling life.

It's important to remember that balance looks different for everyone and it's okay to redefine what it means to us as our lives evolve. With dedication and self-awareness, we can nourish our whole selves and live vibrant, purposeful lives. And in doing so, we can also inspire and positively impact those around us, creating a ripple effect of balance and well-being in the world.

7.4 Self-Care and Self-Reflection

SELF-CARE AND SELF-reflection are essential components of nurturing the whole self. In the fast-paced world we live in, it is easy to neglect our own needs and prioritize the demands of our relationships, careers, fitness routines, and spiritual practices. However, taking the time to care for ourselves and reflect on our experiences is crucial for maintaining balance and overall well-being.

The Importance of Self-Care

SELF-CARE INVOLVES intentionally taking actions to promote our physical, mental, and emotional well-being. It is about recognizing our own needs and making choices that prioritize self-nurturing. Engaging in self-care activities allows us to recharge, reduce stress, and enhance our overall quality of life.

There are various ways to practice self-care, and it is important to find what works best for you. Some examples include:

1. **Physical self-care**: Engaging in regular exercise, getting enough sleep, eating nutritious meals, and taking care of our bodies through practices like massage or yoga.

1. **Emotional self-care**: Nurturing our emotional well-being by expressing our feelings, seeking support from loved ones, engaging in activities that bring us joy, and practicing self-compassion.
2. **Mental self-care**: Taking care of our mental health by engaging in activities that stimulate our minds, such as reading, learning new skills, or engaging in creative pursuits.
3. **Social self-care**: Cultivating healthy relationships and connections with others, spending time with loved ones, and engaging in activities that foster a sense of belonging and community.
4. **Spiritual self-care**: Nurturing our spiritual well-being through practices such as meditation, prayer, spending time in nature, or engaging in activities that align with our values and beliefs.

The Benefits of Self-Care

ENGAGING IN REGULAR self-care practices offers numerous benefits for our overall well-being. Here are some of the key advantages:

1. **Reduced stress**: Self-care activities help to reduce stress levels by pro- viding an outlet for relaxation and rejuvenation. Taking time for ourselves allows us to recharge and better cope with the demands of daily life.
2. **Improved physical health**: Engaging in regular exercise, eating nu- tritious meals, and getting enough sleep are all essential components of self-care that contribute to improved physical health. These practices can boost our immune system, increase energy levels, and reduce the risk of chronic diseases.
3. **Enhanced mental well-being**: Self-care activities that stimulate our minds, such as reading or engaging in creative

pursuits, can improve our cognitive function and enhance our mental well-being. Taking care of our mental health is crucial for maintaining a positive outlook and managing stress.

4. **Increased self-esteem**: Engaging in self-care activities sends a message to ourselves that we are worthy of love and care. This can boost our self-esteem and self-confidence, leading to a more positive self-image.

5. **Improved relationships**: When we prioritize self-care, we are better equipped to show up fully in our relationships. Taking care of ourselves allows us to be more present, attentive, and compassionate towards others.

The Power of Self-Reflection

SELF-REFLECTION IS the process of introspection and examining our thoughts, feelings, and actions. It involves taking a step back from our daily routines and experiences to gain a deeper understanding of ourselves and our lives. Self-reflection allows us to learn from our experiences, make conscious choices, and grow as individuals.

Here are some ways to incorporate self-reflection into your life:

1. **Journaling**: Writing down your thoughts, feelings, and experiences in a journal can help you gain clarity and insight. It allows you to reflect on your day, set goals, and track your progress.

2. **Meditation**: Practicing mindfulness meditation can help you cultivate self-awareness and observe your thoughts and emotions without judgment. It provides a space for reflection and self-discovery.

3. **Seeking feedback**: Asking for feedback from trusted friends, family members, or mentors can provide valuable insights into your strengths and areas for growth. It allows you to gain different perspectives and learn from others' experiences.

4. **Engaging in solitude**: Carving out time for solitude and quiet reflection can help you connect with your inner self and gain clarity on your values, goals, and aspirations.

5. **Setting aside dedicated reflection time**: Schedule regular reflection time in your routine, whether it's a few minutes each day or a longer period once a week. Use this time to reflect on your experiences, assess your progress, and set intentions for the future.

The Benefits of Self-Reflection

ENGAGING IN REGULAR self-reflection practices offers numerous benefits for personal growth and well-being. Here are some of the key advantages:

1. **Increased self-awareness**: Self-reflection allows us to gain a

deeper understanding of ourselves, our values, and our beliefs. It helps us identify patterns, strengths, and areas for growth.

2. **Improved decision-making**: By reflecting on our experiences and ex- amining our thoughts and emotions, we can make more informed and intentional choices. Self-reflection helps us align our actions with our values and goals.

3. **Enhanced personal growth**: Self-reflection provides an opportunity for learning and growth. It allows us to identify areas where we can improve, develop new skills, and make positive changes in our lives.

4. **Better problem-solving**: Taking the time to reflect on challenges and setbacks can help us gain new perspectives and find creative solutions. Self-reflection enhances our problem-solving skills and resilience.

5. **Increased self-compassion**: Self-reflection promotes self-compassion by allowing us to acknowledge and accept our strengths and weaknesses. It

helps us cultivate a kind and non-judgmental attitude towards ourselves.

Incorporating self-care and self-reflection into our lives is essential for nurturing the whole self. By prioritizing our own well-being and taking the time to reflect on our experiences, we can cultivate vibrant lives and create a positive ripple effect in our relationships, careers, fitness routines, and spiritual practices. Embrace the journey of nourishing the whole self and commit to lifelong practices that sustain your well-being.

Conclusion

As we come to the end of our journey together, it is important to reflect on the lessons we have learned and the changes we have made in our lives. Nourishing the whole self is not a one-time task, but rather a continuous journey that requires dedication and effort. It is about creating a balanced and healthy lifestyle that encompasses all aspects of our being – relationships, careers, fitness, and spirituality.

Throughout this book, we have explored the interconnectedness of these four aspects and how they contribute to our overall well-being. We have learned that each one plays an important role in our lives, and neglecting one can have a ripple effect on the others. We have also seen how our diets and food choices impact our emotional, mental, and physical health.

But the journey of nourishing the whole self is not just about making changes in our external practices; it is also about embracing a new mindset and attitude towards our lives. It is about recognizing that we are the authors of our own story, and we have the power to create a fulfilling and vibrant life.

One of the most significant takeaways from this book is the importance of balance. We must find a way to integrate all aspects of our lives, rather than prioritizing one over the others. Building healthy relationships, thriving in our careers, prioritizing fitness, and cultivating spirituality should all have a place in our lives. When we neglect one area, we create an imbalance that can lead to feelings of frustration, stress, and discontent.

This journey is also about embracing the power of choice. We have the power to choose the foods we eat, the relationships we build, the career we pursue, and the spiritual practices we engage in. It is essential to remember that these choices are not just about our physical and material well-being, but also our emotional and spiritual well-being.

Nourishing the whole self also requires patience and perseverance. Change does not happen overnight, and it takes time to build new habits and incorporate healthy practices into our lives. There will be challenges and setbacks along the way, but it is crucial to stay committed to the journey and trust in the process.

Moreover, it is essential to celebrate our progress and accomplishments, no matter how small they may seem. Often, we are quick to criticize ourselves and focus on our shortcomings, but it is equally important to acknowledge and celebrate our growth and successes. By doing so, we can cultivate a positive mindset and continue to move forward on our journey.

As we embrace this journey of nourishing the whole self, it is crucial to remember that it is not a destination but a continuous process. There is no end goal that we strive towards, but rather a lifelong commitment to our well-being. We must continue to learn, grow, and evolve in all areas of our lives, and in turn, we will see the ripple effect in our relationships, careers, fitness, and spirituality.

The journey of nourishing the whole self also involves taking care of ourselves. It is about setting boundaries and prioritizing self-care. We must listen to our bodies, minds, and spirits and give ourselves the time and space we need to recharge and rejuvenate. Self-reflection is also an essential aspect of this journey. It allows us to pause, evaluate our lives, and make necessary changes. By regularly reflecting, we can ensure that we are living in alignment with our values and goals.

As we continue on this journey, we must involve and support others. Building a vibrant life does not just benefit us individually, but it also has a positive impact on those around us. By nurturing healthy relationships, we create a supportive network that can help us through challenging times and celebrate with us in our successes. We can also inspire others to embark on their own journey of nourishing the whole self.

In conclusion, nourishing the whole self is about creating a balanced and vibrant life through healthy relationships, thriving careers, consistent fitness routines, and meaningful spiritual practices. It is a journey that requires dedication, patience, and self-care. But the results are worth it. By embracing this journey, we can experience a deep sense of fulfillment and live our lives to the fullest. Remember, you are the author of your own story, and it is up to you to nourish and cultivate a vibrant, fulfilled, and purposeful life. Embrace the journey, and may it bring you endless blessings and joy.

Creating a vibrant and fulfilling life is not a one-time task, but an ongoing journey. It requires consistent effort, dedication, and commitment to sustain a balanced and healthy lifestyle. In this chapter, we will explore the importance of lifelong practices in nourishing the whole self and how they contribute to sustaining vibrant lives.

The Power of Consistency

CONSISTENCY IS THE key to achieving any goal or maintaining a healthy lifestyle. It is the act of repeatedly doing something over time and sticking to a routine. When it comes to relationships, careers, fitness, and spirituality, consistency is crucial in building and nurturing them.

Consistent effort is required to maintain healthy relationships. This means regularly communicating with loved ones, spending quality time together, and showing them love and support. In our careers, consistency helps us stay on top of our goals and responsibilities, build a good reputation, and continuously improve our skills.

In terms of fitness, consistency is necessary to see progress and reach our health goals. It is not enough to work out or eat healthy every once in a while; we must make it a consistent practice to see long-term results. And when it comes to spirituality, consistent practices such as meditation, journaling, or prayer help us stay connected with our inner selves and the universe.

Building Healthy Habits and Routines

IN ORDER TO SUSTAIN a vibrant life, it is important to establish healthy habits and routines that align with our goals and values. Habits are behaviors that we do automatically without much thought. Routines, on the other hand, are a series of habits that we follow regularly to achieve a certain outcome.

Building healthy habits and routines takes time and effort, but they can have a profound impact on our overall well-being. For example, if we want to improve our physical health, we can establish a habit of exercising for at least 30 minutes every day and incorporate healthier food choices into our daily routines. Over time, these habits and routines will become second nature, making it easier to maintain a healthy lifestyle.

Finding Balance in a Fast-Paced World

IN TODAY'S WORLD, IT can be easy to get caught up in the rat race and neglect our physical, emotional, and spiritual needs. However, finding balance is crucial in sustaining a vibrant life. It means finding a healthy equilibrium between our personal and professional lives, our physical and emotional well-being, and our inner and outer selves.

One way to find balance is to prioritize self-care. This may include activities such as spending time in nature, practicing mindfulness, or engaging in hobbies that bring us joy. It is also important to take breaks from work and disconnect from technology to recharge and rejuvenate.

Another key aspect of finding balance is learning to say no. We often feel pressured to say yes to every opportunity or request that comes our way, but this can lead to burnout and neglecting our own needs. Learning to set boundaries and prioritize our well-being helps us maintain a healthier balance in our lives.

Practicing Self-Reflection

SELF-REFLECTION IS an essential part of sustaining vibrant lives. It involves taking time to reflect on our thoughts, emotions, and actions in order to gain a deeper understanding of ourselves. Regular self-reflection helps us identify areas for growth, celebrate our achievements, and make necessary changes to live in alignment with our values and goals.

Some helpful ways to practice self-reflection include journaling, mindfulness meditation, and seeking feedback from loved ones or mentors. It is also important to cultivate self-compassion and approach self-reflection with a non-judgmental attitude.

The Ripple Effect

WHEN WE NOURISH OUR whole selves through consistent practices, healthy habits, and balanced lifestyles, we not only improve our own well-being, but we also positively impact those around us. Our relationships become stronger, our careers thrive, and we become role models for others to live a more vibrant and fulfilling life.

This ripple effect can also extend beyond our immediate circle and impact our communities and even the world. When we prioritize our health and happiness, we are able to show up as our best selves and create positive change in the world around us.

Final Thoughts and Call to Action

IN CONCLUSION, SUSTAINING vibrant lives through relationships, careers, fitness, and spirituality requires consistent effort, building healthy habits and routines, finding balance, and regular self-reflection. These practices not only benefit our individual well-being but also contribute to the greater good. It is never too late to start cultivating these practices and embark on a journey of whole self-nourishment. I encourage you to take the lessons and tools from this book and apply them in your daily life to create a more vibrant and fulfilling lifestyle. Remember, you have the power to design your own life and nourish your whole self to live a happy and meaningful life.

As we have explored in this book, our relationships, careers, fitness, and spiritu- ality are all interconnected and play a vital role in our overall well-being. When one aspect of our life is out of balance, it can have a ripple effect on the others. This is especially true when it comes to our diets.

Think about it - if we are not getting enough sleep due to a stressful job, our energy levels will be low, making it harder to find the motivation to exercise or make healthy food choices. This, in turn, can affect our relationships as we may have less patience and energy to connect with our loved ones. It can also impact our spirituality as we may struggle to find the time and energy for practices such as meditation or mindfulness.

On the other hand, when we prioritize and nourish our relationships, careers, fitness, and spirituality, we create a positive ripple effect throughout all areas of our life. Our relationships become stronger and more fulfilling, our careers are more aligned with our values and bring a sense of purpose, our fitness goals become more achievable, and our spirituality helps us find inner peace and balance.

But where does our diet fit into this picture? Our diet has a significant impact on our emotional, mental, and physical health, making it a crucial component of nourishing the whole self. Here are some ways in which our diets can create a ripple effect on our overall well-being:

Improving Emotional Well-being

HAVE YOU EVER NOTICED how your mood can change after eating certain foods? Foods high in sugar and unhealthy fats can leave us feeling lethargic, irritable, and even anxious. On the other hand, a diet rich in whole, nutrient-dense foods can help stabilize our moods and promote feelings of happiness and contentment.

This ripple effect is especially crucial in our relationships. When we are in a positive and stable emotional state, we are better equipped to communi- cate effectively, empathize with others, and handle conflicts with patience and understanding.

Enhancing Mental Clarity and Cognitive Function

OUR BRAINS NEED PROPER nourishment to function at their best. Foods that are high in antioxidants, healthy fats, and essential nutrients can improve our cognitive function and help prevent age-related cognitive decline.

This has a significant impact on our careers and productivity. When our minds are clear, and our cognitive abilities are enhanced, we can focus better and make more sound decisions. This can lead to increased job satisfaction and success in our careers.

Fueling the Body for Physical Performance

FOOD IS THE FUEL THAT powers our bodies. Just as a car needs the right fuel to run efficiently, our bodies need the right nutrients to perform at their best. Eating a balanced diet rich in whole grains, lean proteins, and fruits and vegetables can provide us with the energy and stamina we need to take on our fitness routines.

This, in turn, has a positive ripple effect on our physical health. Regular exercise can help prevent chronic diseases, improve our cardiovascular health, and increase our overall strength and stamina. When we feel physically strong and capable, we have the energy and confidence to take on the challenges of our daily lives.

Creating a Vicious or Virtuous Cycle

OUR DIETS CAN ALSO create a vicious or virtuous cycle in our lives. If we constantly turn to unhealthy foods for comfort or as a coping mechanism, it can lead to weight gain, poor health, and a negative self-image. This, in turn, can affect our relationships, careers, and overall well-being.

On the other hand, if we cultivate a healthy and balanced relationship with food, it can create a positive ripple effect on all areas of our life. When we fuel our bodies with nutritious foods, we feel better physically and mentally, which can lead to positive self-image and confidence. This, in turn, can improve our relationships and career success as we show up as our best selves.

The Power of Mindful Eating

ONE WAY TO CULTIVATE a healthy relationship with food and create a positive ripple effect in our lives is through mindful eating. This practice involves being fully present and aware of our food and the act of eating.

By paying attention to our food and our body's signals, we can learn to eat when we are hungry and stop when we are satisfied, rather than eating for emotional reasons. This can help us make better food choices and improve our overall health and well-being.

Incorporating Mindful Eating into Daily Life

IN OUR FAST-PACED WORLD, it can be challenging to find the time and mental space to practice mindful eating. However, with some simple strategies, we can incorporate this beneficial practice into our daily lives:

- Slow down and take time to enjoy your meals without distractions such as phones or TV.

- Pay attention to the flavors, textures, and smells of your food.

- Chew your food thoroughly and savor each bite.

• Listen to your body's hunger and fullness signals and stop eating when you are satisfied, rather than when your plate is empty.

• Practice gratitude for the nourishment your food provides and the effort put into growing and preparing it.

• Choose nutrient-dense, whole foods that will nourish your body and mind.

By incorporating these habits into our lives, we can create a positive ripple effect that will improve our relationships, careers, fitness, and spirituality.

Conclusion

IN THIS CHAPTER, WE have explored the impact of our diets on our overall well-being and how it can create a ripple effect in all areas of our life. By prioritizing and nourishing our relationships, careers, fitness, and spirituality, we can create a positive cycle that enhances our health and happiness.

We have also discussed the power of mindful eating and how we can incorporate this practice into our daily lives to cultivate a healthy relationship with food.

As we wrap up this journey of nourishing the whole self, let us remember the interconnectedness of all aspects of our lives and the importance of balance and self-care. By nourishing our body, mind, and spirit, we can truly thrive and live vibrant lives. Let us continue to make positive choices and create a ripple effect that spreads to those around us.

As we come to the end of this book, it's important to reflect on the key concepts and practices that we have discussed. Nourishing the whole self is a journey that requires constant effort and dedication, but the rewards are well worth it. In this final section, we will review the main takeaways and provide a call to action for you to continue making positive changes in your life.

Throughout the book, we have explored the interconnectedness of relationships, careers, fitness, and spirituality. These four aspects of our lives are essential in nourishing the whole self because each one plays a unique and important role in our overall well-being. We have learned that having healthy relationships is crucial for support, communication, and emotional well-being. Thriving in our careers means finding purpose and balance, and taking care of our physical health through exercise and nutrition is vital for our mental and physical well-being. Lastly, cultivating spirituality allows us to connect with our inner selves and the world around us.

We have also discussed how our diets and food choices play a significant role in our overall health. Our bodies and minds need the right nutrients to function properly, and certain foods can even improve our emotional, mental, and physical well-being. By incorporating a variety of healthy foods into our diets, we can nourish our whole selves and achieve balance in our lives.

One of the main takeaways from this book is that all of these aspects – relation- ships, careers, fitness, spirituality, and food – are interconnected. Neglecting one area can have a significant impact on the others and ultimately affect our overall well-being. Therefore, it is crucial to pay attention to all aspects and strive for balance and harmony in our lives.

Now that we have a better understanding of the importance of each aspect, it's time to take action. Here are some steps you can take to start nourishing your whole self today:

1. Reflect on your current relationships, career, fitness routine, and spiritual practices. Are you satisfied with these areas of your life, or do they need improvement?
2. Identify one aspect that you want to focus on improving. It could be strengthening a relationship, setting career goals, starting an exercise routine, or exploring different spiritual practices.
3. Set realistic and achievable goals. It's essential to have a clear idea of what you want to achieve and how you will get there. This will help you stay motivated and focused.
4. Create a plan of action. Break down your goals into smaller, manageable tasks that you can work on every day. This will make your goals more attainable and help you stay on track.

1. Practice self-care and self-reflection. Taking care of yourself is crucial in nourishing the whole self. Make time for activities that bring you joy, unwind and de-stress, and reflect on your progress and growth.
2. Be open to change and adjustment. As you continue on your journey, keep in mind that you may need to make adjustments and pivot along the way. Embrace change and be flexible in your approach.
3. Surround yourself with positivity and support. Having a strong support system is essential in achieving our goals. Surround yourself with people who support and uplift you, and let go of toxic relationships.

By following these steps, you will be on your way to achieving a balanced and vibrant life. Remember, change takes time, and it's okay to make mistakes. The most important thing is that you are actively working towards nourishing your whole self.

As we conclude this book, we want to leave you with a final thought – the ripple effect. When we focus on nourishing our whole selves, we not only improve our own lives, but we also have a positive impact on those around us. Our relationships flourish, we become more fulfilled in our careers, we radiate positive energy, and we inspire others to do the same. By taking care of ourselves, we can create a ripple effect of positive change in the world.

We hope that this book has inspired you to make positive changes and embark on a journey of nourishing your whole self. Remember, it's never too late to start, and small steps lead to significant progress. We believe in you, and we are rooting for your success. Now it's up to you to take action and continue on this path of holistic well-being. We wish you all the best on your journey, and we hope that you live a vibrant and fulfilled life.

Don't miss out!

Visit the website below and you can sign up to receive emails whenever Mr. Miller publishes a new book. There's no charge and no obligation.

https://books2read.com/r/B-A-LCJBB-WDEQC

BOOKS 2 READ

Connecting independent readers to independent writers.

About the Author

Besides being an artist of fine-arts & audiovisual productions; a strong curiosity in botany has lead the aspirations to become a student of nature. I've sought & still seek as much knowledge as I can about plants, our connections to them, and the many uses of them. It wasn't until the year of 2012 where I watched my father go through extreme debilitating issues with his health. These issues became increasingly painful physically & emotionally for him. With the help of my sister, we were able to help him change his lifestyle and eating habits. Immediately we saw positive results in his health that were undeniable.

Although we all made a neccessary lifestyle change, it was unfortunately inevitable for my father to progress on. What was believed to have been food poison turned into what doctors concluded to be stomach cancer. After dealing with the grief, deep pain, isolation, and numerous negative thoughts; I made the decision to invest in the world of balanced living. To gain more knowledge, I took advantage of certification programs and schooling for nutrition. With the knowledge that I've gained and utilize, I've set out to not only help my family, but to be of great service to my community as well. May my research and efforts to help see a healthier community cause a ripple effect on everyone everywhere.

Empower your mind, nurture your body, and ignite your soul. There Is More To Accomplish.